ORCHIDS
AND OTHER AIR PLANTS
of the
Everglades National Park

By
Frank C. Craighead

Published in cooperation with the
Everglades Natural History Association
UNIVERSITY OF MIAMI PRESS
CORAL GABLES, FLORIDA
1963

1

DEDICATION

For my many friends, those amateur naturalists of southern Florida, who are so keenly interested in the preservation of the unique plant and animal life of the Everglades.

Acknowledgments

Some twelve years ago a Park herbarium was initiated by Mr. W. E. Dilley, Park Naturalist, and Dr. W. B. Robertson, now Park Biologist. In 1953, the writer, having retired from the U.S. Department of Agriculture, accepted the suggestion that he should continue the work. The collection has gradually increased to include about 1000 species of the area. Especially helpful in this project were Mr. Vincent J. Mrazek, District Ranger at Flamingo and later at Key Largo, 1953-1957, and Naturalists Clay L. Gifford and V. C. Gilbert. Mrs. V. C. Gilbert made most of the drawings.

Until 1955, Mr. Roy O. Woodbury of the Botany Department of the University of Miami identified many of the plants, particularly while we were on field trips together. Later, much of the herbarium material was identified by Dr. Erdman West and Miss Lillian Arnold of the University of Florida, Gainesville. Dr. Monroe R. Birdsey of the University of Miami, was helpful in making comparisons with specimens in the University herbarium. Dr. T. G. Yunker of DePauw University, Greencastle, Indiana, determined the peperomias and Dr. Lyman B. Smith of the Smithsonian Institute, Washington, D.C. the bromeliads.

Many of the photographs were taken by the author's sons, Drs. F. C., Jr. and J. J. Craighead, on visits to the Park, some were obtained from Dr. Monroe R. Birdsey, Carl A. Luer, M.D., Sarasota, Florida, and the remainder taken by the writer. Drs. Taylor R. Alexander and Monroe R. Birdsey of the Botany Department, University of Miami, Dr. W. B. Robertson, Dr. J. G. Stout, University of Florida, and Mr. Bruce Beeler read and gave constructive criticism of the manuscript. Professor Floyd H. Shuttleworth was helpful with the sections dealing with the orchids. Mr. William J. Olafson, University of Miami, materially assisted in editing the manuscript.

Several life time residents of the Homestead area aided materially in locating plants. Among these were Messrs. Fred J. Fuchs, Sr., and Fred J. Fuchs, Jr., noted for their interest in orchids and skill in growing them, and Mr. and Mrs. Glenn Simmons, former residents of Flamingo.

Introduction

This is the second book planned by the Everglades Natural History Association. It is the first to treat the plants. It is the intention of the Association to present a series of papers on various aspects of the unique natural history of the Everglades National Park. The first was *Everglades — The Park Story*, by Dr. William B. Robertson.

A purpose of this book is to acquaint visitors to the Everglades National Park with some of the characteristic plants, in this case those that grow on trunks and branches of trees. These are called epiphytes or air plants. They are a distinctive feature of the area and a constant source of interest and inquiry by visitors. Some ferns, orchids, peperomias, bromeliads, one cactus, and a tree have become adapted to an aerial mode of living and are discussed in this book. In addition, this unique area with its tropical vegetation and unusual plant societies, is briefly described.

The plan of this book follows a somewhat different approach from that used in several manuals which describe the plants of other National Parks. Instead of trying to encompass the entire Park flora at this time when our knowledge of the plants is still incomplete, separate publications covering certain habitat groups such as the epiphytes, the vines, plants of the pine land, and the saw-grass glades, is considered more advisable. This permits a more popular treatment, placing emphasis on the illustrations rather than on technical descriptions. The latter have been reduced to a minimum but when used with the drawings and photographs, should be sufficient for recognition of the different species.

The characters used to identify species are chiefly those that can be seen most of the year, especially those that are recognizable in the field. Thus, in considering orchids and air plants, more importance is attached to the flower stalks, leaves, and seed pods. which remain on the plant through most of the year, than to the flowers which may last but a day.

The size of these plants varies enormously, depending on age and environment. Measurements given here are based on the writers experience with mature flowering plants found in southern Florida. Many of these species grow more luxuriantly in the tropics.

The flowering period varies in this tropical area. The seasonal blooming characteristic of temperate zone plants is not so well defined here. It is as though many never accept a winter rest and keep on blooming with every rise in temperature. The botanist Small (1929) called Florida "the land of perpetual bloom." Flowers and fruits can be seen at any time on many species while others have only a short blooming period. The flowering dates given here are based on wild plants, primarily those within the park boundaries. Plants brought into the greenhouse, watered and fertilized, bloom irregularly often when no flowers can be found in the wild.

The families of plants that have developed the epiphytic habit are few and readily recognizable and no attempt is made to characterize them fully. Few technical terms are used, so no glossary is provided. This information is available in several National Park floras and other botanical works (Harrington and Durrell, 1957).

Table of Contents

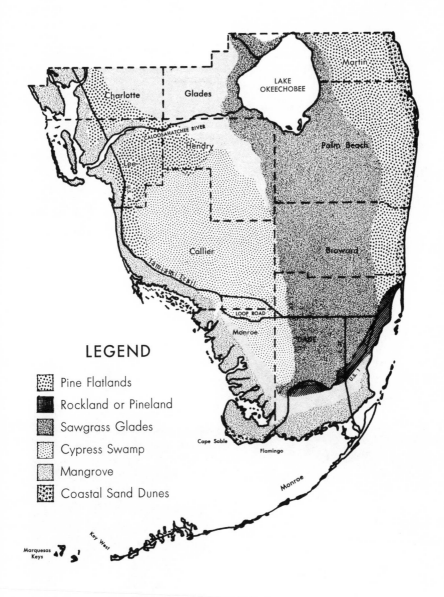

FIGURE D-1. — Map of southern Florida showing principal vegetation types and physical features.

FIGURE 1. — The Everglade Trail bisects a broad expanse of sawgrass.

FIGURE 2. — The sawgrass abruptly changes into a forest of thickly growing pines.

Vegetation Of The Everglades

The Everglades National Park occupies about one and one-half million acres near the extreme southern tip of the Florida peninsula and includes most of the islands in Florida Bay and along the west coast to Everglades City. The Everglades proper is a much larger region extending northward from the Park across the Tamiami Trail to and around Lake Okeechobee. This includes practically all the central portion of southern Florida.

The Park has many of the physical and biotic features of the larger Everglades region. In addition, it has a greater abundance of the tropical plants which characterize this area and set it apart from any other section of the United States. Here the climate is milder and over the years has permitted the establishment and growth of many species of plants from the West Indies. This is especially true of the warmer portions such as the Florida Keys, along the east and west coasts and particularly in the hammocks with their protected climate. This climatic zone is known as sub-tropical Florida, or as suggested by Robertson (1955), tropical Florida. It includes all of the Everglades National Park and extends northward in a gradually narrowing strip along both coasts; on the west approximately to Charlotte Harbor and on the east to Palm Beach, although a few species extend still further north.

The Everglades country is flat, so flat that it is difficult to detect any movement in the water that covers the greater part of it except for tidal fluctuations or, to the experienced eye, the "flow" of the aquatic plants in the glades and fresh water creeks. An occasional shell mound along the coast may rise five to 25 feet. The scenery of the Park, if such a term applies, can be observed best from the air and appears as a gigantic jig-saw puzzle made up of great expanses of grassy water dotted with numerous islands and interlocked plant masses.

Thus it is really the flora that is distinctive, that shapes the landscape and contributes to the strangeness of the Everglades. Here unusual plants are massed together in strangely characteristic formations. There

11

FIGURE 3. — The thin soil is underlain by the rock of the Miami oolite formation in which these pines are anchored.

are no vast fields of brilliant color flaming with great numbers of blooms, such as those which adorn the prairies of middle and north Florida or the valleys or mountain slopes of other National Parks.

Some of the different plant societies can be seen as one drives from Homestead to Flamingo on the new road that bisects the Park. At one time he may be passing through extensive areas of sawgrass, rooted below a continuous sheet of water (Fig. 1). Abruptly, there is a change to a forest of pine trees (Fig. 2) which, on closer inspection, are seen to arise from a rough rocky floor (Fig. 3). Just as suddenly the scene changes to a landscape of bizarrely-shaped cypress trees (Fig. 4) protruding from the grassy water as far as the eye can see. In winter these cypress trees are leafless and give the appearance of being long dead as they stand "skeleton-like" and bleaching in the tropic sun.

Farther on, as the water becomes brackish, small scattered, umbrella-like shapes appear (Fig. 5), propped above the water on arched roots. These, the mangroves (Fig. 6), become more and more numerous, growing larger and larger as the coast is approached until finally they form an impenetrable wall (Fig. 6, 7).

More than 20 plant associations of southern Florida have been described by various botanists (Davis, 1943). However, only the more important types need to be mentioned for present purposes. (Fig. D 1). One of these, the mangrove belt, occupies a crescent-shaped area of salty-to-brackish waters all around the coast. It extends inland beyond Whitewater Bay where it is some 15 miles across, and comprises about one-half the area of the Park.

Three species of mangrove, red, black, and white, make up this forest. The red mangrove margins the coasts and perimeters of the keys. It faces the ocean, catching debris from the tides and storms and advances the shore line outward to make new land. Black mangroves frequently fringe the coast but more commonly, mixed with white, grow in low inland areas where the salt content of the soil is often much greater than that of the sea. White mangrove occurs in pure stands resulting from flooding waters which float the numerous seeds onto a suitable soil.

The buttonwood is a common associate of the mangrove trees. It forms hammocks on accumulating humus deposits only a few inches higher than the low ground occupied by the mangroves. Few epiphytes grow on the red and black mangroves though some are found on the white. In the buttonwood hammocks of this zone and in the scrub mangrove area farther inland are to be seen some of the richest assortments of these plants.

Throughout the mangrove belt are islands of slightly elevated marl, shell, or humus accumulations, only one to three feet high. These are leevee-like stream banks, coastal prairies and shell and sand beaches. Some shell mounds are 25 feet in height. All of these elevations support growths of tropical hardwoods, called hammock forests, quite in contrast to the mangrove vegetation surrounding them.

Farther inland the great expanse of fresh-water lowland supports other plant societies. The cypress belt is an extensive area of swampy low-land dominated by dwarf or giant cypress called domes, sloughs, or strands. This forest association extends diagonally across the Park from southeast to northwest and across Collier County.

FIGURE 4. — Bizarrely-shaped scrub cypress skeletons cover a large expanse of the area.

In the southeastern portion, on the thinner soils along the Flamingo highway, the cypress is dwarfed, though perhaps just as old as the giant trees in Collier County. This Collier County area is often called the "Big Cypress Swamp" and includes such remarkable associations as the "Fahkahatchee Strand" and "Corkscrew Swamp." This whole cypress belt is rich in air plants and orchids, perhaps more species occurring in the Fahkahatchee Slough than in any other area of similiar size in southern Florida.

The glades or sawgrass prairies (Fig. 1), occur on slightly higher land than the cypress or mangrove associations. This is a land of marl or muck soil which is under water much of the year. Some portions, depending on elevation and rainfall, are dry during some winters. The glades have a distinct and characteristic flora. The dominant species are sedges and grasses but many marsh plants, representing a number of families, are typical.

Some of these plants are obvious only during the dry season, others only when the glades are flooded. Here also hammocks are scattered about on slight rock elevations or humus accumulations. The flora of the higher rock hammocks resembles that of the pine land while low hammocks, often called bay heads, support trees and shrubs that can withstand flooding for many months, and marsh plants that can tolerate shade.

The rock land or pine land (Fig. 2) forms the higher barrier to the east of the glades. Within the park its maximum elevation is only seven feet above sea level, but in places farther north toward Miami it exceeds 20 feet. The dominant plant is slash pine (*Pinus elliottii*). Its abundance is due to the fact that it is not seriously damaged by the frequent fires that sweep this land. The pine land is rich in other fire resistant plants, some of which are found in other plant associations (Robertson, 1953). This pine land is spotted with islands or hammocks (Fig. 8) of denser growth formed by tropical hardwoods mixed with a few northern species.

Where this pine land is broken into islands such as Long Pine Key and Pine Island, the term "The Everglade Keys" has been applied. The southern-most of these keys meets brackish water near Mahogany Hammock where a few living pines have survived the slowly rising waters of Florida Bay. Here many bleaching and decay-resistant poles still stand to mark the site of a pine key.

In addition to these plant communities, several geographic subdivisions have been designated by earlier botanists. Some of these are convenient for present purposes. The Florida Keys are the islands of the long barrier reef originating north of Miami and extending south

FIGURE 5. — As the waters become brackish, scattered umbrella-like shapes appear. These are the mangroves.

FIGURE 6. — The mangroves eventually merge into an impenetrable wall.

FIGURE 7. — The mangrove roots loop out to trap debris and build up the floor of future hammocks.

FIGURE 8. — The pineland is spotted with hammocks, or islands of dense growth, composed of tropical hardwoods.

to Key West and on to the Marquesas and the Dry Tortugas Islands. The term "Lower Keys" is often used for the islands from Big Pine Key south. Many of these lower islands are outcrops of the oolitic limestone of the mainland, while the "Upper Keys" are coral rock. Between the Florida Keys and the mainland is a broad area of shallow water dotted with numerous low islands, known as The Florida Bay Keys. These are composed of marl. They are fringed with a belt of mangroves or occasionally with shell beaches supporting hammock growth.

The Cape Sable Region (Fig. 9) as referred to in early botanical literature included the Flamingo Prairie. Present usage restricts the name to the three capes; the East Cape, Middle Cape, and Northwest Cape including the hammocks and mangroves touching the shores of Lake Ingraham. The Flamingo Prairie (Fig. 10) is a marl flat rising slightly along the coast and merging into mangroves to the north. It is covered with grass or shrubby vegetation and scattered buttonwood hammocks, extending from the East Cape Canal to Snake Bight Canal. Much of this prairie was cleared by the charcoal operations and by the cultivation of the early settlers. The abundance of tree snail shells in the soil indicates that much of it was formerly covered by trees. Behind Lake Ingraham and Little Sable Creek is an area of similar vegetation which is often referred to as the Raulinson Prairie.

East of Flamingo, the Maderia Hammock area which extends to U.S. Highway 1, is also a marl flat elevated one to two feet. It is broken by lakes and creeks and patches of prairie but is for the most part covered with the remains of extensive hardwood hammocks. Formerly this forest contained an abundance of high grade mahogany, but over the past three centuries they have been removed by logging and fires. Only the decay-resistant stumps and fallen logs attest to the former excellence of this stand.

The Big Cypress, particularly that portion known as the Fahkahatchee Swamp, contains many species of epiphytes. This remarkable area has been feelingly described by Buswell (1937), as follows:

"One of the most interesting spots in all Florida is the wild orchid gardens of the Big Cypress forest. A green-roofed cathedral with columns decorated, often from base to top, with orchids, ferns and other epiphytic plants. A labyrinth of leafy aisles through giant ferns, beautifully draped stumps and cypress knees and an occasional woodland pool. During the late summer months when there are frequent rains these slightly lower spots are more or less under water, but wading is quite refreshing in this tropical forest. At other times the ground is fairly dry and, as the water prevents the rank

17

growth of vines and shrubs that are almost impassable on the higher ground outside, the walking is much easier at all times of the year. Only a botanist would be willing to climb and push and crawl through miles of thorny vines and dense shrubbery to gain admission to this cathedral, but to some it is well worth the price. . . .

"In all of the area of the proposed [Everglades] National Park there is no other spot where so many rare plants are found and the only spot in the United States where we can see and realize the wonderful beauty of a tropical jungle. Mammoth Royal Palms are scattered through the forest, the green plumes often far above the other trees. After spending a day in a spot like this the man-made parks outside seem very artificial and uninteresting."

FIGURE 9. — Northwest Cape Sable showing beach, hurricane dunes and hammock in the rear.

FIGURE 10. — The Flamingo Prairie is a marl flat bearing grass and shrubs, bordered by buttonwoods.

18

What Are Air Plants?

An air plant or epiphyte may be defined as a plant growing upon another plant using the latter only as a support. Though living on other plants, it is not a parasite, because it obtains no nourishment from its host as do the true parasites.

The epiphytic adaptation has developed among several great divisions of the plant kingdom. It might seem that nature, pleased with her first attempt at devising such an ingenious adaptation for occupying neglected sites, proceeded to use it for several of her evolutionary diversions, among them ferns, orchids and even some trees. There are many other less conspicuous epiphytic plants such as the algae, mosses, and lichens. These are not described here.

When we consider the many species of plants that grow upon trees, shrubs, or logs and try to decide whether this is or is not an epiphyte, the above definition needs elaboration.

Plants that are fastened high on trees or woody shrubs are typical epiphytes. Other epiphytes may grow nearer the ground and even extend aerial roots to the soil. In this case when the young plant originates above ground and not in the soil, it seems logical to consider it an epiphyte. Some ferns send up runners along the sides of stumps and fallen logs and new plants originate from these runners. These also are treated as epiphytes. Finally there are those species which normally exist on the humus layer of the forest floor in fresh water areas but in the brackish mangrove swamps they grow only on logs or trees. These also are treated as epiphytes. Occasionally some, such as Spanish moss and ball moss which normally fasten high in the branches of trees, attach themselves to rocks, old buildings and even to the wires of fences and telephone lines.

The bromeliads and the orchids are the most numerous and conspicuous epiphytes of this region. Various common names have been ascribed to them. "Air plant" is used for both groups. "Wild pine" is applied to some bromeliads because of the resemblance to their relative, the pineapple. The most common and distinctive species have been given names as noted in the text.

True epiphytes are highly specialized plants. Their various structures have been greatly modified through evolutionary processes, losing some functions and developing others that are not normally performed by the same organs of terrestrial plants. The "roots" anchor the plants to their support, but also absorb water and minerals from the substrata. Several orchids, among them the ghost flower, are essentially all roots, these organs having assumed the additional function of manufacturing food. They concede only the power of reproduction to the few flowers supported on a short stem.

Living in an atmosphere that fluctuates between extremes of humidity and drought, epiphytes have had to make adaptations for the conservation of moisture. The simplest modification is to reduce the number and size of leaves. Further adaptive development is thickening and covering the leaves with a heavier, tougher epidermis or skin, thus reducing the loss of water through transpiration. Many orchids are provided with thickened stems called pseudobulbs which store large quantities of water. Another adaptation among many bromeliads is an arrangement of the leaves into a rosette. The individual leaves are shaped so as to collect and hold rain and dew in a cup-like reservoir at the base.

Few of the epiphytic ferns are found far removed from deep shade where moisture is more abundant. Consequently these plants show little modification in structure. There is one which may be considered an exception. The resurrection fern (Fig. 25), has developed the curious ability to contract and curl its leaves when adverse conditions arise. Provided in this way to meet adversity, the fern can climb higher onto the sunlit branches. When the weather becomes too dry, too windy, or even too cold, it curls up exposing the brown undersurface until "awakened" again into green freshness by rain or heavy night-time dew.

There is still another adaptation to the specialized life of an epiphyte. To insure perpetuation of the species it was necessary to provide some effective means whereby the seeds would reach the branches of the host. The chances of a seed lodging in a crevice on the bark of a tree are indeed small compared to those of terrestrial species whose seeds are carried to the moist earth by gravity.

Ferns meet this challenge by producing millions of dustlike spores, light enough to drift in the gentle breezes of the hammock. Nature uses her successful devices over and over again. The orchids in adopting this same means of dissemination, produce the smallest seeds of any flowering plants. The number of tiny dustlike seeds produced in a single large capsule such as that of the cow-horn orchid, has been estimated at several million. The vanilla orchids, however, are an exception. They have small round seeds, too heavy to be blown about by air currents.

The bromeliads use another device common among plants. Their seeds are provided with feathery plumes (Fig. 28, 29) which act

FIGURE 11. — Twisted air plant. *Tillandsia circinata*.

FIGURE 12. — Stiff-leaved wild pine. *Tillandsia fasciculata*.

as "parachutes" counteracting gravity and permitting them to drift for great distances. On dry windy days, when the seed pods are bursting, the air may sparkle because of the light reflected from clouds of these tiny, shining, drifting parachutes. The fuzzy plumes catch and hold firmly to the rough tree bark.

The release of these seeds is properly timed. The pods remain green throughout the summer, gradually draining sustenance from the whole plant as it dies slowly during the following winter. Then late in the dry season, as stiff March breezes sweep the flat Everglades, these browning pods split and the seeds are ejected. Many perish but a few catch and cling to the rough bark. They have only a short while to wait until cloudy skies and warm spring rains provide conditions suitable for germination and survival.

Only one cactus, the mistletoe cactus, has become adapted to an aerial mode of living. It has still another modification to insure distribution of its seeds. Each fruit contains several seeds which, when ripe, are enclosed in a sticky gelatinous matrix, much like that of the mistletoe, a similarity which suggested the common name for this cactus. Birds feed on these seeds and carry them on their beaks or feet to other trees where they are preened off, germinate and start a new plant. This would appear to be a more effective method of dissemination, as relatively few seeds are produced by this plant.

The seeds of the strangler fig also are embedded in a sticky matrix, adapting them to animal distribution. When the fruit is ripe it is a favored food of birds and mammals. These seeds, as well as those of the cactus, may be distributed in the droppings of animals. Peperomia seeds are carried on an upright spike and have a peculiar adhesive property that insures prompt atachment to any objects that touch them. Raccoons have a favorite habit of walking along the tops of fallen logs, where they pick up quantities of seed on their hairy coats to be brushed off later at new locations.

Most of our native epiphytes have another means of reproduction, the vegetative method. These, with the exception of the one air plant, produce growing tips from buds along the rhizomes or stems of the old plant which develop into new individuals. This method is sure and reliable, often resulting in large colonies (Fig. 11, 12) of closely grouped plants that give the clumpy appearance to many bromeliads and orchids. However, this is strictly a means for local multiplication and does not provide for dispersion into distant hammocks.

Where The Epiphytes Grow

Epiphytes are migrants from the warm humid climate of the Tropics. By far the greatest number are confined to that part of southern Florida where a near tropical climate exists. A few have acquired modifications to meet more adverse moisture and temperature conditions and are found farther north, some in central or northern Florida and even beyond.

Only one of the epiphytic orchids, the green-fly orchid, has gotten beyond the Florida state boundary as far north as the Carolinas and westward along the coastal plain to Louisiana. Two species are found in mid-peninsular Florida, *Harrisella*, and the butterfly orchid. About a half dozen grow in the Florida Keys, chiefly on Key Largo and northward. They are not abundant here due possibly to the dry winters.

The bromeliads are much hardier and are found at greater distances from their tropical origin. About half of our species extend north midway into peninsular Florida; one of them, Spanish moss, ranges along the coast to Virginia, this and ball moss are found westward along the moist coastal plain to Texas. Few grow in the Florida Keys except on Key Largo and the islands just north.

Few of the truly epiphytic ferns extend beyond southern Florida though one of the filmy ferns has been found in the northwestern part of the state. The plume fern also is found in central peninsular Florida. The resurrection fern is an exception, extending throughout the southeastern United States as far north as Iowa and Pennsylvania.

Most epiphytes reach their finest development in the dim light of the hardwood hammocks and cypress sloughs (Fig. 13, 14). However, some species of orchids have left this shady environment and moved out into the bright sunlight. These seem quite well adjusted to living on the smaller oaks or dwarf cypress forming the margins of the hammocks or sloughs, on dwarf mangroves of the brackish waters, and on the scattered buttonwood, pond apples, willows or cocoa plums of the glades.

FIGURE 13. — Many air plants reach their best development in the dim light of the hammocks.

FIGURE 14. — Some species have left their arboreal environment and seem equally adjusted to the rock floor.

The butterfly orchid grows large in the shade but its flowers and leaves lack the brilliance of those growing in the sun on dead button-woods. The cowhorn orchid likewise prefers sunshine where it grows to a large size. When its increasing weight crushes its support and the plant drops into the shade beneath, it gradually dwindles in size, fails to flower, and finally succumbs.

More of the bromeliads have adjusted to sunny sites. The twisted, banded and stiff-leaved air plants, the ball moss, the yellow catopsis and the giant air plant, all are more vigorous and more brilliantly colored where light is abundant. Perhaps their efficient dew condensing mechanisms and leaf funnels for water storage permit them to defy the drying sun and stiff winter breezes of these exposed locations.

Low temperatures are of great importance in restricting the occurrence of epiphytes. Only a few grow north of the line of frequent frost. Killing frosts occur even in extreme southern Florida at intervals of five to 10 years. The destructive effects of these frosts may be extremely local. A slight swale or depression of only one foot may serve as a focus for collecting cold air sufficient to freeze and girdle the host plants just above the ground (Alexander, 1958).

Tropical plants that push northward during a series of warm winters are suddenly set back by these freezes. The royal palm was reported by Bartram during his travels in 1765-1767 to be growing as far north as Lake George, Florida (Harper, 1958).

The cold weather of January, 1956, destroyed many orchids, especially the dollar orchid, in the Flamingo area where the thermometer registered a minimum of 29 degrees F. In general the dry glades are the coolest. The pine woods are a little warmer, but here too, many of the low level plants freeze. During cold waves the hammocks are the warmest places by several degrees which explains why many tropical plants exist and thrive in these well insulated "houses."

Another important factor in the distribution of these plants is variation in rainfall both from the wet to the dry season and from year to year. The heavy precipitation which ranges from 50 to 80 inches or more during spring, summer and fall provides the high atmospheric humidity that many of these plants require. But the relatively dry winters, especially of the Florida Keys, may restrict their distribution. Humidity is normally higher and more congenial in the hammocks because the leafy canopies present a barrier to the desiccating winds and midday sun of winter's cloudless skies.

Fire has been an important factor in the life and death of the hammocks and the epiphytes they support. Normally the hammocks were reasonably fireproof. The frequent burning of the glades and pine lands from lightning and by the Indians did relatively little harm because the high moisture content of the hammock humus stopped fires at the edge. After a succession of drought years aggravated by a lower water table which was the purpose and result of the drainage canals, the humus layer became dry and flammable.

At such times, notably in the late thirties and again in the early fifties, the deep humus of many fine hammocks caught fire and slowly burned, destroying practically all plants. Massive trunks of mahogany, oak, lysiloma and mastic, two to four feet in diameter, still lie on the floor of many of these hammocks, rotting evidence of their former glory and man's thoughtlessness. Robertson (1955) made a thorough study of the effects of fires in southern Florida and has found them to be one of the most important ecological factors shaping the life history of the pinelands and the hammocks.

Hurricanes are an equally potent and destructive factor in shaping the pattern of vegetation in this region. In fact it can be said that the beginning and end of the mangrove forests are the results of this force. In the Flamingo area, 25 years after the 1935 hurricane, there is still ample evidence of the destruction it caused. The remains of the so-called "black forest" are evident in the occasional large trees that have survived and in the many decay-resistant, prostrate trunks on the ground.

Hurricane Donna swept over some 120 square miles of the mangrove belt on September 9-10, 1960. The catastrophic destruction left in the wake of this storm belittles any imaginary picture compiled from the remaining evidence of earlier storms. Today over much of this area, the forest is dead, a tangled, broken and twisted mass (Craighead and Gilbert, 1962).

The air plants, orchids and ferns are gone, except for occasional individuals that somehow miraculously escaped. Over 90 percent of the epiphytes vanished, torn off the trees by 36 hours of continuous winds, which veered around the compass. They were then pushed into decomposing windrows by the accompanying tidal wave or smothered with inches of sticky marl brought in by the sea water. Many of the epiphytes that held their positions on trees were later burned by the winter sun beating down on them through leaf-less branches.

One year after Donna passed the beginnings of the new forests were evident. Many of the seedlings of red and black mangrove survived. Seeds of white mangrove were ripe at the time and formed a scum of germinating seedlings on the receding waters. Now the seedlings of these three species are growing vigorously along with those of many salt tolerant herbs and shrubs giving the appearance of rapid recovery. Now two years later, still more deceptive is the vast greenery resulting from several species of vines spreading rapidly over the dead skeletons. During the two years following Donna's passage these vines have draped many square miles with a green shroud. However encouraging this illusion may be, it will require 50 to 100 years to restore the epiphytes in the mangrove belt to anything like their former abundance.

There are several other agents which destroy epiphytic plants and locally affect their abundance. Many bromeliads are destroyed by raccons, especially during the dry winter months. These animals tear them from the limbs of trees in search of the water and frogs concealed in the cup-like bases of the leaves. The raccoons often eat the succulent "buds" of mature plants as they start to elongate into flower stalks. Deer are fond of nibbling at the succulent flower stalks of orchids and those bromeliads having soft-textured leaves. Rodents often gnaw the pseudo-bulbs of orchids, insects frequently bore into the flower spikes. Some specific cases of these injuries are mentioned later under the discussion of the species.

A characteristic feature in the distribution of some epiphytes is their marked preference for certain species of host trees. In the hammocks of the Everglade Keys where the live oak is a predominant tree, epiphytic plants crowd together in such masses that larger branches may be completely covered. In the sloughs, the trunks and branches of the cypress and pond apples furnish the principal supports, and in the brackish water areas, it is the buttonwoods.

Where the ground is slightly elevated and buttonwood grows in pure stands, the epiphytes thrive and cover the bark to such an extent that individual trees seem almost to merge together. It appears that the rough bark of these favored hosts, oak, cypress, and buttonwood, offers a better trap and lodgement for the drifting, wind-borne seeds. In addition, as the bark of these trees grows thicker and rougher, it does not readily slough off and thus supplies a firm anchorage for many years. It has also been suggested that barks of some trees may have special nutritional value that stimulates these epiphytes. More likely it is simply that these rough barks collect and hold more organic debris.

Paradise Key, often called Royal Palm Hammock, was formerly the site of many species of plants not found there at present, according to records of earlier visitors (Simpson, 1932, Small, 1929). Fires, hurricanes, and vandals have robbed posterity of much of the hammock's beauty. Indeed, few fine hammocks remain in the area. Under the protection of the National Park Service it is hoped that nature will in time be able to restore some of the glory that prevailed when white man first came into this hammock.

All orchids and bromeliads, except Spanish moss, and several trees and shrubs, are protected under the conservation laws of Florida. The statutes make it a misdemeanor to buy, sell or remove these plants from public land and from private land without the written consent of the owner. Unfortunately it has been difficult to enforce this law.

FIGURE 15. — Mahogany hammock just before hurricane Donna shattered most of the larger mahoganies.

FIGURE 16. — Solution holes are a characteristic feature of rock land hammocks.

Everglades Hammocks

Scattered throughout the several plant associations of this area are rounded humps of trees, the so-called domes, houses, or hammocks (Fig. 15). These often rise 60 feet and are most conspicuous in the sawgrass prairies where they rise abruptly from the water level. Hammocks protrude as domes above the scrubby cypress, but among the taller pines and mangroves they appear, at first sight, merely as denser and darker tangles.

Hammocks are most simply defined as islands of tropical hardwoods within or surrounded by a contrasting plant association. Instead of hammocks, possibly the term "houses" is more suitable, implying protection and maintenance of warm, moist conditions suitable for luxurious growth of epiphytes. Certainly the higher humidity, freedom from extremes of temperature, the protection from desiccating winds and sufficient elevation to insure good drainage, are characteristic features of hammocks (Alexander, 1955).

Much of the mystery of the Everglades, so feelingly expressed in the folk-lore and literature of this country, must have originated from these dark shaded jungles that abruptly obstruct one's passage in any direction whether through the mangroves, the saw grass glades or the rockland. The neophyte instinctively bends his course to go around these obstructions. Gradually curiosity overrides his apprehension and he parts a way through the brush-walled exterior to reach the shaded recesses within. The cool, friendly serenity of the interior is soon appreciated and more and more he alters his course to reach and penetrate that darkened dome on the horizon in the assurance that there will be revealed some plant or animal never seen before, or some deep solution hole concealing tragedies of the past.

The solution holes or sinks are a characteristic feature of the rockland hammocks (Fig. 16). They are supposed to have resulted from the gradual leaching of the soft limestone by organic acids produced during the decay of leaf litter. The deeper holes often contain the partly fossilized remains of animals which during the past several thousand years were trapped and have become buried in the accumulating humus. Skeletons of most of the mammals, turtles, snakes and some birds of the region, including even vultures, are found here. (Bird, 1953).

A common characteristic of all hammocks seems to be elevation. This raised area may be composed of any of several materials, humus, marl or rock. Even the slight ridge forming at the edges of a bulldozer trail in constructing a fire line through the glades is occupied by seedlings of hammock plants in the next growing season. A few years later, if undisturbed, this trail will be outlined by a row of shrubs and trees.

Older residents who frequented the glades for hunting and trapping, tell of hammocks starting on a mound or windrow of organic debris such as that deposited by the receding waters of heavy rains or hurricanes. The lowering of the water level in the glades by the drainage canals is changing the character of the broad expanse of sawgrass to a landscape spotted with brush and tree islands.

In the brackish mangrove belt, the hammocks form on a layer of humus a few inches to a foot or more thick, resting on top of the marl. Humus acts like a sponge, holding a layer of fresh rain water floating just above the salt for much of the year. Often the remains of the original red mangroves that started the humus accumulation can be seen in these hammocks indicating relatively rapid build up.

The shallow depth of this fresh water layer is attested by the root behavior of the vegetation. Wind-thrown trees reveal the roots spread out in a perfectly horizontal plane only six to ten inches below the surface. Indians, fishermen and hunters have long taken cognizance of this adaptation. They saw off the trunks of dead wind-falls four to five feet above the roots, then plant the trunks with roots uppermost. Boards are then placed on the flat roots to provide a camp table.

KEYS AND DESCRIPTIONS

Most of us learn to recognize objects by a visual picture or impression. Usually this picture lacks detail, the mind being content to group similar objects, such as birds, snakes or trees. If members of any given group are encountered frequently, the more curious and observant person will note differences among them. Gradually, as curiosity is further aroused and understanding increases, the seeker is led by the desire to find and recognize more and more variations.

Because of the many species of plants included in this book it would be a considerable task for the Park visitor to search through all the figures every time he wishes to identify a plant. Therefore, keys have been prepared which, it is hoped, will provide an aid in this search among the illustrations.

Turning to the first number of the appropriate key, the visitor is confronted with alternatives, and he must decide which alternative fits the plant he has found. At each step in the key there are two or more alternatives from which to choose.

Whichever alternative is chosen, the number to the right indicates which number to select. Whatever number is stated, the next step in the key is to move immediately to that number, ignoring all intervening steps. In some cases, the name of the plant will be found after two or more numbers have been chosen; in other cases, several numbers must be used before arriving at the correct name of the plant.

RIBBON FERN
Paltonium lanceolatum

31

BROMELIADS
on dead buttonwood

32

A. Mule Ear Orchid

B. Pineland Spike Moss

C. Peperomias

D. Mistletoe Cactus

PLATE 12

A. Stiff-leaved Wild Pine   B. Reddish Wild Pine

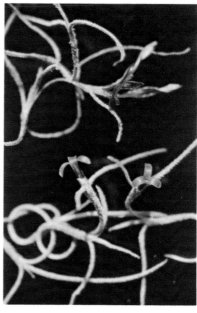

C. Reflexed Wild Pine   D. Spanish Moss

PLATE 13

B. Slender-leaved Wild Pine   C. Butterfly Orchid

A. Cowhorn Orchid

D. Green Fly Orchid

PLATE 14

A. Worm Vine

B. Hand Fern

C. Strap-leaved Bromeliad

D. Hoary Air Plant

Plate 15

A. Ghost Orchid   B. Variegated Oncidium

C. Campylocentrum   D. Night Blooming Orchid

PLATE 16

A. Reddish Peperomia

B. Dollar Orchid

C. Florida Oncidium

D. Ionopsis

PLATE 17

A. Spread Eagle Oncidium   B. Brown Epidendrum

C. Trinidad Macradenia   D. Pale Flowered Polystachya

PLATE 18

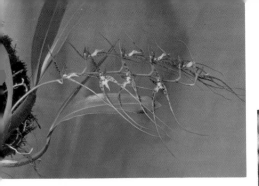

A. Spider Orchid

B. Clam Shell Orchid

C. Worm Vine

D. Oblong-leaved Vanilla

PLATE 19

The Families Of Epiphytic Plants

Descriptions of 74 species of epiphytic plants, representing ten families, are discussed here. Seventeen of these are ferns and for convenience, two of the lower vascular plants formerly classified as fern relatives are included, the whisk fern and the spike-moss. The remainder are flowering plants, also known as seed plants. Among the latter are included: 16 bromeliads or air plants; 31 orchids; four peperomias; one cactus and two trees.

These make up the more conspicuous epiphytes that are such a characteristic feature of the plant life in sub-tropical Florida. There are also many less conspicuous epiphytes among the lower plants such as lichens, algae, and mosses. These are not included in this discussion.

EPIPHYTIC FERNS

One of the most enthusiastic lovers of Florida plants, John K. Small, said in his book, *Ferns of Florida* (1931),

> "Florida has been called 'the land of flowers'; even more properly could it be called the land of ferns. While its pine lands and prairies are themeselves not without their own peculiar species, its woods, hammocks, marshes, swamps, and sand dunes so abound in fern plants, often in such remarkable luxuriance, that Florida becomes the Fern State, par excellence, among all the states of the Union."

Over 100 species of ferns have been recorded from the State of Florida. These include approximately one-third of all the species found in North America. Nearly 60 of the Florida species are of tropical origin and are confined to the southern part of the State. Some species are restricted to the pine land, others to the glades or the cypress swamps. A few species are aquatic but by far the greatest number are found in the hammocks, especially those of the Everglades Keys.

Where the orchids and bromeliads give a grace and suffused beauty to the trunks and spreading tops of the hammock trees, the ferns add a cool greenness to the humus floor. They cover old decaying logs with a green shroud suggesting the burrows of a giant mole. They line the rough edges of solution holes with a green drapery that lures the visitor to lie on the ground and peer into the concealed depths.

There is a definite tendency among the epiphytic ferns for some species to grow almost exclusively on certain host plants. Thus the palmetto or cabbage palm is the most common host for the hand fern, serpent fern and grass fern. The resurrection fern is more commonly found on live oak trees while the cypress fern usually grows on cypress knees and the ribbon fern on mangroves near salt water. Others are more indiscriminate growing on dead logs, in knot holes or cavities, or even on the forest floor.

Ferns might be called plants of the past. They were in their day of glory and abundance during the coal ages, especially the Carboniferous Period, some 200 million years ago, according to estimates of the geologists. These prehistoric plants grew in great luxuriance in a congenial climate. Extensive forests of shrubs and giant trees covered the ground with dense vegetation, probably much like the tropical rain forest of today. Some of these extinct plants were close relatives of our living club mosses but they grew to tremendous size when contrasted with existing species.

Fossil club mosses have been found with trunks three to five feet in diameter and nearly one hundred feet tall. Their dead trunks and foliage accumulated in thick beds of organic matter. These were later covered by layers of mineral deposits and compressed to form the several types of coal that have contributed to the industrial development of this country.

Key to the Epiphytic Ferns

1. Plants bearing very small scales or scale-like
   leaves on the stems 2
   Plants with larger leaves of various shapes 4

2. Erect plants with green, angular stems that
   branch in pairs .... Whisk Fern
   Psilotum

   Low plants forming a moss-like mat over the
   surface of their attachment 3

3. Leaves upright from a creeping root-stock .... Filmy Fern
   Trichomanes

   Leaves scale-like, in two ranks on an upright
   stem .... Spike Moss
   Selaginella

4. Vine-like climbing fern with several leaf
   shapes varying from oval to linear .... Vine Fern
   Phymatodes

   Plants not vine-like 5

5. Plants pendant from their point of attachment 6
   Plants upright; leaf tips often arched 7
6. Leaves broad, palmately lobed; spore-bearing organ
   a separate structure near base of leaf blade .... Hand Fern
                                                              Ophioglossum
   Leaves long and narrow, grass-like .... Grass Fern
                                                              Vittaria
7. Leaf blades undivided, usually strap-shaped,
   several times longer than wide 8
   Leafy blades deeply divided 10
8. Sori borne on modified tip of leaf .... Ribbon Fern
                                                              Paltonium
   Sori distributed over the leaf blade 9
9. Sori round .... Strap Fern
                                                              Campyloneuron
   Sori linear in parallel rows, set obliquely to
   the mid-rib .... Nest Fern
                                                              Asplenium
10. Leaf blades broad, about twice as long as wide;
    sori not covered by the indusium 11
    Leaf blades several times longer than wide 13
11. Leaflets not completely divided to mid rib .... Serpent Fern
                                                              Phlebodium
    Leaflets completely divided and slightly
    stalked 12
12. Sori in distinct rows .... Brazilian Polypody
                                                              Goniophlebium
    Sori closely massed .... Cypress Fern
                                                              Meniscium
13. Sori not covered by indusium 14
    Sori covered .... Boston Fern, Sword Fern
                                                              Nephrolepis
14. Leaflets bearing numerous scales beneath .... Resurrection Fern
                                                              Phymatodes
    Leaflets without scales .... Plume Fern
                                                              Polypodium

THE WHISK FERN
Family Psilotaceae

The Whisk fern found in southeastern United States, and a related species of the Eastern Hemisphere, are the only living members of this family. Fossil species of the Lower Devonian Period, some 300 million years ago, have been found to be so similar to present day plants that the whisk fern has been termed a living fossil. These plants and related species are believed to be the first plants to have developed the upright habit of growth and internal structures that characterize higher plants. Formerly they were classified with the ferns but are now considered to represent a much more primitive group (Milne, 1959).

WHISK FERN
Psilotum nudum (L) Griseb. (Fig. 17)

A rather stiff, dichotomously branched plant, four to 18 inches tall, with angular, slightly winged stems which bear scattered tiny scale-like "leaves" about ⅕ of an inch long. The sporangia are sessile, borne at the bases of small scales in three-lobed, three-celled globular masses about ⅕ of an inch wide and of a lemon to orange color.

The Whisk fern is a humus-loving plant, growing around the base of trees, on well rotted logs or in humus-filled cavities of trees. Its stiff angular much branched stem bearing numerous orange sporangia make for easy identification.

It occurs commonly in moist shaded woods throughout Florida and north through Georgia into South Carolina. It is widespread in tropical America.

SPIKE MOSS
Family Selaginellaceae

These creeping, moss-like plants appear at first glance more like true mosses than ferns. They are more closely related to the club-mosses than to the true ferns. Two kinds of spores are produced in the axils of slightly modified leaves which form four-sided "cones" at the tips of the branches. Some species occur in deep, moist shade where they form mat-like coverings on logs, tree bases, and rims of solution holes. Others are found in the sandy pine lands. Several species are recorded from this area, but only one is commonly an epiphyte.

FIGURE 17. — Whisk fern. *Psilotum nudum.*

PINELAND SPIKE MOSS
Selaginella armata Baker (Fig. D5, P12B)

A creeping moss-like plant bearing yellow-green leaves of two different shapes and set in two planes. The larger are broadly oval, ¹⁄₃₂ to ¹⁄₁₆ inch long and abruptly pointed while the smaller are awl-shaped. The spore-bearing cones are about ⅛ inch long. They are formed of ovate, spine tipped bracts and terminate the branches.

This light-green, moss-like plant grows most abundantly on the rocks of low brushy pine land. When the water recedes it grows rapidly and covers the tops of exposed rocks. In dry periods it seems to disappear or at least it is difficult to find. It also lines walls of solution holes and grows on the roots and stems of trees in these sinks.

THE HAND FERN
Family Ophioglossaceae

The hand fern is the only epiphytic representative among the three genera of this family found in southern Florida. These ferns have globular sporangia developed on a separate stem which branches from the leafstalk. The leaves of these three genera show wide variations in structure, some of which are fern-like in character while others are quite aberrant.

FIGURE 18. — Filmy fern. *Trichomanes kraussii.*

FIGURE D-2. — Resurrection fern. *Polypodium polypodioides.* Rootstalk, leaves and sori. (¼ actual size).

FIGURE D-3. — Hand fern. *Ophioglossum palmatum.* Leaf and sporangia. (¼ actual size).

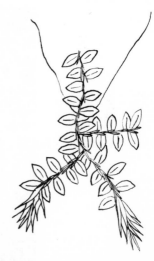

FIGURE D-4. — Filmy fern. *Trichomanes krausii.* Rootstalk and two leaves, one bearing the tubular indusium. (2 times actual size).

FIGURE D-5. — Spike moss. *Selaginella armata.* Showing two ranked leaves and spore-bearing cones at tips of branches. (2 times actual size).

HAND FERN
Ophioglossum palmatum L. (Fig. D3, P15B)

The pendent, palmately lobed, yellow green leaves of this fern hang in groups of two to ten from white fleshy roots embedded in the dead leaf bases of cabbage palmettos. The fronds or leaf blades are 12 to 18 inches long, two to eight-fingered, broad, limp and somewhat fleshy. The spore-bearing structures consist of a double row of bead-like sporangia borne on a well-defined stalk.

The hand fern is appropriately named. It is a tropical species once fairly common in Florida but now relatively scarce in most localities. This fern is particularly susceptible to damage by fire because of the flammability of the palmetto leaf bases among which it grows. It has survived only in the more moist portions of the dense hammocks which have escaped fires. Mr. W. R. Llewellyn, of Christmas, Florida, has called attention to extensive feeding by squirrels on the succulent roots in dry weather.

THE FILMY FERNS
Family Hymenophyllaceae

Our filmy ferns are delicate matted plants with thin, almost transparent leaves. Several species are recorded from Florida, one of which is often epiphytic.

FILMY FERN
Trichomanes kraussii Hook & Gre. (Fig. 18, D4)

This plant forms a fluffy dark green mat over the surface of the rocks, in lime sinks, and on logs. The thin, nearly transparent leaves are ¼ inch to one inch long, on hairy petioles, entire[2] lobed, or even deeply dissected when mature and the margins bear several black, stiff, curved bristles. The sporangia are borne inside a tubular, two-lipped structure (indusium) on the upper edges of the leaf.

The thick, bright green mat characteristic of this plant suggests a moss more than a fern. It is found only in very moist hammocks where it covers the walls of solution holes, and surfaces of roots and branches which have fallen into these sinks. In dry weather the mat crumples and is hardly recognizable. Small (1931) records several species in the Everglade Keys and one in northwest Florida. However, they are now rarely seen in southern Florida. The extensive fires of recent years have no doubt eliminated them from much of their former range.

---

[2]Always intimately associated with this species is a form with undivided leaves which may represent *T. punctatum Poir.*

FIGURE 19. — Nest fern. *Asplenium serratum.*

FIGURE 20. — Strap fern. *Campyloneuron phyllitidis.*

THE TRUE FERNS
Family Polypodiaceae

This family includes many species which show great variations in form and structure as well as diversity in the habitats they occupy. Our most conspicuous and common ferns, those typically fern-like in appearance, belong to this group. The fronds are entire or pinnate, the latter often subdivided two to four times. The new leaves are tightly curled in the early stages of growth forming the so-called "fiddleheads." These gradually unfurl as the leaf develops. The sporangia or spore-bearing organs are borne on the underside of the leaflets in variously shaped groups called sori. They may be covered with the "indusium" or exposed.

BIRDNEST FERN
Asplenium serratum L. (Fig. 19)

A relatively large fern with linear-lanceolate, undivided leaves twelve to thirty inches in length somewhat resembling those of the strap fern but have serrate margins. The leaves are closely grouped at the base and ascend in a spreading and arched funnel-like form. There is often a distinctive coppery-irridescent sheen to the leaves. The sori form narrow linear stripes on the under surface of the leaf and are set at an angle of about 45° to the mid-rib. The sori are covered.

The birdnest fern is so called because its arching leaves form a deep nest-like hollow usually filled with leaves and debris. The characteristic coppery, irridescent color makes this plant a striking and distinctive feature of the Big Cypress Swamp. It is found also in deep shade in the larger hammocks of the Everglade Keys. It grows on stumps, logs, and trunks of trees, and less commonly, on the forest floor. This fern has been collected extensively and used as a house plant.

STRAP FERN
Campyloneuron phyllitidis (L) Presl. (Fig. 20, D6)

A relatively large fern that has long, slender, strap-shaped, arching and undivided leaves, often 36 inches in length arising in a group from the short rootstock. The petioles are short, the lateral veins prominent and parallel, set slightly oblique to the mid-rib. The sori alternate in rows on each side of the lateral veins and have no covers.

This is the largest of several strap ferns in the area. It is abundant, often covering logs and stumps with its long, gracefully arched leaves.

Three other epiphytic species of this genus have been found in the area but are not very common.

THE NARROW-LEAVED STRAP FERN
Campyloneuron angustifolium (Sw. F'ee)

This strap fern is quite distinct with its long narrow and rather thick leaves, eight to 20 inches in length and ½ to ¾ inch wide, tapering

FIGURE 21. — Cypress fern. *Meniscium reticulatum.*

41

FIGURE 22. — Sword fern. *Nephrolepis biserrata.*

to each end. The veins are indistinct. The sori are arranged in a single row on each side of the mid-rib.

Small (1931) records it from Timms Hammock in Dade County. Recently specimens have been found in Collier County.

Campyloneuron costatum (Kunze) Presl.

This strap fern is characterized by leaves which have slender, tapering tips and rather long petioles. They are leathery and shiny and the veins are obscure. It occurs on cypress logs and knees in Collier County.

THE SMALLER STRAP FERN
Campyloneuron latum Moore

This is a much smaller fern than *C. phyllitidis*. In addition it has a more elongate and distinct petiole. Small (1931) reported that he found it in the Hattie Bauer Hammock in Dade County. The writer has been unable to locate any specimens of this species.

BRAZILIAN POLYPODY
Goniophlebium brazilense (Poir.) Farwell (Fig. D7)

The brazilian polypody somewhat resembles its relative the golden polypody, but is smaller, having leaves from eight to 20 inches in length. The rootstocks are covered with brown scales and the slightly stalked leaf segments are divided completely to the mid-rib.

This species has been reported but once in a very limited range on the west coast of Florida in the vicinity of the Ten Thousand Islands. It has not been seen by the writer. The sketch (Fig. D7) has been adapted from Small (1931).

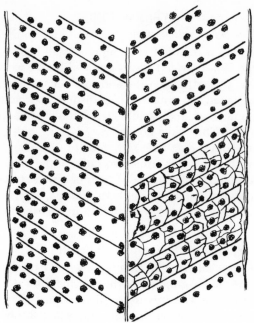

FIGURE D-6. — Strap fern. *Camplyoneuron phyllitidis.* Section of leaf showing veination and sori. (slightly enlarged).

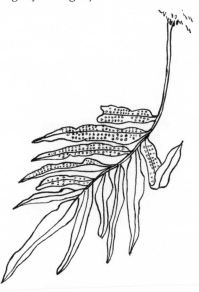

FIGURE D-7. — Brasilian polypody. *Goniophlebium brasiliense.* Leaf showing sori and fully divided leaflets. (¼ actual size).

CYPRESS FERN
Meniscium reticulatum (L.) Sw. (Fig. 21, D8)

This large fern is reported to be nine feet tall but is usually about half that height. It has divided leaves grouped from a woody base. The leaflets are short-stalked, lanceolate, four to 15 inches long, the margins irregularly wavy, and the primary veins distinct and parallel. The sori are large and numerous, and usually completely fill the space between the primary veins. They have no covers.

This is our largest epiphytic fern, much resembling the terrestrial leather ferns with which it is often associated in the cypress sloughs. It is usually perched on the knees and stumps of cypress trees. It has been reported to occur throughout southern Florida, but in the writer's experience, it is now rare and restricted in its distribution.

SWORD FERN
Nephrolepis biserrata (Sw.) Schott (Fig. 22)

This is a very tall fern, its fronds sometimes reaching 15 feet in length. These are closely grouped on the rootstock and at intervals along the extensive runners. The leaves are divided once and are elongate, arching or more often twining through supporting shrubs. The leaflets are closely spaced and have strongly serrate margins. The sori, are arranged in two parallel rows along the margin of the leaflet and, when young, are covered with a circular indusium.

This very abundant fern is usually terrestrial, but also grows on stumps and logs. It forms extensive mats of fronds along the edges and more open spaces of hammocks. Often these are difficult to walk through, or more properly to walk over, as the fronds must be crushed down to permit travel. Small (1931) records specimens having fronds reaching a length of 27 feet, but the largest seen by the writer were 15 feet. The sword fern occurs throughout the area and is especially abundant in the Everglade Keys.

BOSTON FERN
Nephrolepis exaltata (L.) Schott

The Boston fern is commonly associated with the sword fern and is often confused with it. It is smaller, the fronds rarely becoming eight feet long. The leaflets have slightly crenulate rather than serrate margins and bear triangular auricles or lobes at the base.

This fern is usually terrestrial, often densely covering the ground along the margins of hammocks and in burnt out places. In the more shaded hammocks, it is often found growing high, in forks or on stubs of trees or among leaf stalks of palmettos, usually higher than the serpent fern.

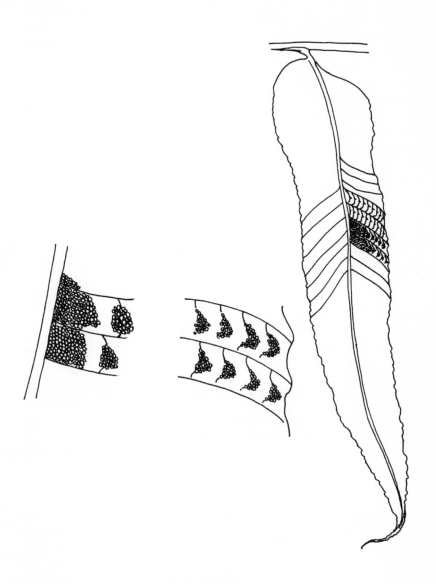

FIGURE D-8. — Cypress fern. *Meniscium reticulatum*. Leaflet and sori enlarged.

RIBBON FERN

Paltonium lanceolatum (L.) Presl. (Fig. D9)

The ribbon fern has tufted, narrow, elongate, somewhat fleshy leaves varying from four to twelve inches long and ¼ to ¾ inch wide, rather erect, but the longer ones are arched. The sori are concentrated in two bands occupying the constricted tip of the leaf.

This is a rare epiphyte, apparently restricted in distribution in this country to a few of the Florida islands, Elliott, Largo and Old Rhodes Keys. It has been found recently on Key Largo, Monroe County, where it was growing on the trunk of mangrove trees near salt water.

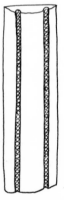

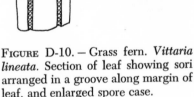

FIGURE D-9. — Ribbon fern. *Paltonium lanceolatum*. Leaf showing sori grouped at end. (1.5 times actual size).

FIGURE D-10. — Grass fern. *Vittaria lineata*. Section of leaf showing sori arranged in a groove along margin of leaf, and enlarged spore case.

GOLDEN POLYPODY, SERPENT FERN

Phlebodium aureum (L.) J. Smith (Fig. 23, D13)

This is a large fern, having thick rootstocks that are covered with golden reddish hairs and intertwined among the leaf bases of the cabbage palm, or more rarely, among the irregularities of some rotten log or stump. The leaves vary from 15 to 48 inches in length and arise singly from the rootstock. The petioles are long and the broad leaf blade deeply incised almost to the mid-rib. The sori are large and arranged in two series, one on each side of the mid vein of the leaflet. They have no cover (indusium).

46

FIGURE 23.—Serpent fern. *Phlebodium auredum.*

FIGURE 24. — Plume fern. *Polypodium plumula.*

47

This large and showy fern seems almost as much an integral part of the cabbage palm in southern Florida as are the fronds of its host. A large percentage of these palms support the golden polypody which hides the rough leaf bases of the upper palm trunk with its copious foliage. In winter the leaves fall. Then its golden rootstocks, pockmarked with the conspicuous leaf-scars, are readily visible. It is widely distributed throughout central and south Florida, in the Florida Keys as well as in tropical America.

VINE FERN
Polypodium heterophyllum L. (Fig. D11)

The vine fern is readily recognized by its slender climbing rootstocks which are covered with reddish scales and are tightly affixed by aerial rootlets to the trunks of trees or shrubs. The leaves are widely spaced along the stem, entire and slenderly petioled. The juvenile ones are broadly oval; in the adult stage they are more elongate, reaching a length of three to five inches. The sori are relatively large, round, and arranged in two parallel rows along the mid-rib. They are not covered.

The vine fern is widely distributed but only locally abundant in moist hammocks through southern peninsular Florida and Key Largo. It is rather uncommon within the Park boundaries. It may climb ten feet or more up the trunks of trees. Under favorable conditions it may cover all the smaller stems over a considerable area, producing a very pleasing effect.

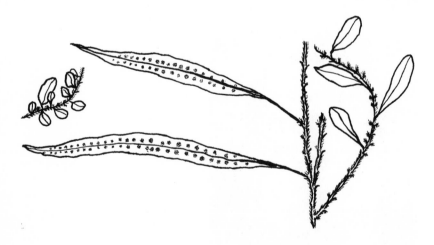

FIGURE D-11. — Vine fern. *Polypodium heterophyllum*. Climbing rootstock and leaves of variable size. (natural size).

FIGURE 25. — Ressurrection fern, *Polypodium polypodioides*, in dry weather, growing on a dead cabbage palm.

FIGURE 26. — Resurrection fern. *Polypodium polypodioides*, after a tropical shower.

PLUME FERN
Polypodium plumula Humb. & Bonpl. (Fig. 24)

This graceful fern is characterized by slender, curved, arching fronds which are wide in the middle and taper to each end. They are four to 24 inches long, once divided with many narrow, closely spaced segments. The sori are round with no covers (indusia) and are two-ranked midway between mid-rib and leaf margin.

This fern is reported over much of south Florida, including the Florida Keys. In Everglades National Park it has been found of late only in the denser hammocks at the junction of fresh and brackish waters. It is one of our most attractive ferns, covering old logs with gracefully arched and finely pinnate, dark green fronds. It is very susceptible to fire which probably explains its elimination from much of its former range.

RESURRECTION FERN
Polypodium polypodioides (L.) Watt. (Fig. 25, 26, D2)

This fern is characterized by long, scaly, creeping rootstocks which are firmly attached to the bark of trees and from which single leaves arise at spaced intervals. These leaves are four to twelve inches long, once divided near the mid-rib. The leaf segments are bright green above but grayish-brown beneath because of the covering of numerous

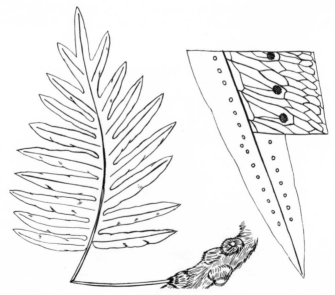

FIGURE D-13. — Serpent fern. *Phlebodium aureum.* Rootstock showing leaf scars, leaf (⅙ actual size) and sori (slightly enlarged).

FIGURE 27. — Grass fern. *Vittaria lineata.*

round to comet-shaped scales. The veins are obscure. The sori are round and without covers (indusia), and are borne in two rows near the margin of the leaflets.

The resurrection fern is probably the most common and widely distributed epiphytic fern of the area. It covers branches, trunks, and logs of hammock trees in dense masses of bright green or brown fuzzy-like growth. It is sometimes called the poor man's hydrometer; the fronds are curled and brown in dry weather, but quickly expand and return to their vivid green color after a rain. It extends northward as far as Pennsylvania and Iowa and is found throughout Florida and tropical America.

GRASS FERN, SHOE STRING FERN
Vittaria lineata (L.) J. Smith (Fig. 27, D10)

This fern has dark green, grass-like leaves which are grouped and hang in tufted pendants from the trunks of the cabbage palm or, rarely, from some other support. They often reach 24 and occasionally 40 inches in length but are only ⅛ to ¼ inch wide. The sori are borne in two long, narrow rows in a groove near the under edges of the leaf.

The grass fern is strictly epiphytic, usually growing on trunks of cabbage palmetto and associated with the golden polypody or the hand fern in the few places the latter still exists. It occurs commonly throughout southern Florida and the upper Florida Keys wherever the cabbage palm grows, provided there is sufficient shade and moisture. It is abundant in the hammocks of the Everglades Keys but is rapidly disappearing in many localities.

FIGURE 28. — Yellow catopsis. *Catopsis berteroniana.*

THE BROMELIADS, WILD PINES, OR AIR PLANTS
Family Bromeliaceae

The bromeliads are commonly called wild pines, because of their resemblance to the edible pineapple. Nearly a thousand species have been found and described but only sixteen are known to grow wild in Florida. Our native bromeliads are all epiphytes, but many of them thrive equally well when they fall to the ground. The pineapple, the best known terrestrial bromeliad, rarely produces seed. It has not become established in Florida. At one time, however, it was cultivated extensively here. Occasionally a pineapple plant takes root and grows when the leafy tops, discarded from our kitchens, fall on suitable soil.

There is a general similarity of form among most of our bromeliads. Usually the stiff leaves are clustered into a compact rosette at the base of the plant from the center of which emerges a flower stalk. This rosette of spreading basal leaves forms a cup that serves to collect water and hold debris from which some of the plant's nutrients are obtained. These wide-spreading cupped leaves are especially well adapted to funneling rain or dew. Even in the driest of seasons they collect and hold considerable water. Nearly a pint of water may be obtained when some of the larger plants are overturned. This water may be potable when boiled but one's thirst must be sufficiently acute to overlook its slight coffee color and the miscellaneous occupants, for they are usually inhabited by numerous mosquito wrigglers or other insect larvae, and small tree frogs (Neill, 1951).

On the other hand Florida's most common air plant, Spanish moss, which is not a true moss, is markedly different from other bromeliads or air plants, hanging as it does from the branches in long festoons. Ball moss, a close relative, is intermediate in form between these extremes.

Air plants are usually attached to the main trunk or branches of rough barked trees and shrubs by modified roots. Spanish moss clings to its support because its copious festoons are draped and thoroughly

FIGURE 29. — Many-flowered catopsis. *Catopsis floribunda.*

FIGURE 30. — Reddish wild pine. *Tillandsia polystachia.*

tangled around and over the twigs, but ball moss grows around and around the twigs like a loose watch spring. It would seem that the ball moss has the better device for attachment; at least more plants of Spanish moss than ball moss cover the ground in the aftermath of storms.

The forest floor of certain hammocks may be densely covered with certain species of bromeliads. Just why these plants grow in abundance on the humus floor in some hammocks is not easily explained. However, in such places there is generally a preponderance of trees which have scaly bark, such as poison wood, that flakes off as the tree grows. The seeds of air plants readily catch and germinate on these trees. Later the plants drop with the separation and fall of the bark scales. In the descent the leaves, acting like parachutes, settle the plants gently, roots first, on the damp humus where they readily adapt to their new situation.

The flower spikes are distinctive features of these plants. They project a few inches to six or seven feet from the basal rosette of leaves. During flowering, they are clothed in colorful bracts varying from pastel shades of white, green or yellow to the most brilliant shades of red. These beautiful bracts are commonly mistaken for flowers. Actually the latter are almost wholly concealed behind these bracts. Three petals of various colors, blue, purple, white, or yellow, protrude from the contrasting sepals and bracts. The petals may last but a day before they wither. The capsules or seed pods then develop rapidly. They usually grow beyond the sepals for ¼ to ¾ of their length, then remain apparently dormant over winter or even a full year while the seeds within slowly mature. The plant remains green during this time.

In winter months the leaves of these fruiting plant wither in most of our native species, the pods split, and masses of plumed seeds are released from their capsules to drift with the wind.

All our native species can be briefly characterized as epiphytes, with perfect flowers composed of three sepals, three petals, three to six stamens, and a single pistil. The fruit is a capsule which splits into three parts to disperse numerous plumose seeds.

Key to the Bromeliads

1. Seed capsule ovoid, slightly longer than wide 2
   Seed capsule cylindrical, length two or more
   times its width 4
2. Corolla yellow, flower stalk drooping .... Small catopsis
   Catopsis nutans

   Corolla white 3
3. Leaves yellowish-green, upright; flower
   stalk erect .... Yellow catopsis
   C. berteroniana

   Leaves dark green, thin, tips of leaves and
   flower stalk drooping .... Many-flowered catopsis
   C. floribunda
4. Plants matted together in festoons; flower
   stalk about ½ inch long .... Spanish Moss
   Tillandsia usneoides

   Plants matted together in ball-like clumps;
   flower stalk 2 to 6 inches long .... Ball Moss
   T. recurvata

   Plants distinct individuals, often grouped,
   but stems and leaves not intertwined 5
5. Flower stalk concealed completely by bracts 6
   Flower stalk exposed between bracts which do
   not completely overlap 13
6. Leaves constricted above the base, then
   spreading to form an urn-shaped base 7
   Leaves widely spread from base, forming
   a rosette 10
7. Flower stalk short, rarely 6 inches long;
   small, compact forms 8
   Flower stalk longer 9
8. Leaves hoary, covered with reflexed scales .... Hoary air plant
   T. pruinosa

   Leaves gray-green, not scaley .... Twisted air plant
   T. circinata

55

FIGURE 31. — Ball moss. *Tillandsia recurvata.*

Catopsis

Three species of the genus *Catopsis,* all of the epiphytic type, are found in the Everglades Park. They closely resemble the firm-leaved or true air plants, and are in fact more easily recognizable as individual species than as a generic group. They do have a few characteristics in common, among these are the shorter, less colorful, and less closely appressed stem bracts which never completely cover the flower stalk; a short, stout, ovoid seed pod; correspondingly shortened and less tubular sepals and petals; a very short style, bearing a trilobed stigma; and stamens that are not exserted beyond the corolla.

YELLOW CATOPSIS
Catopsis berteroniana (Schult) Mez (Fig. 28, D14)

The yellow catopsis has distinctive, glaucous, yellow-green leaves forming a cylindrical upright body, from which arises a tall, upright flower stalk, 20 to 40 inches in length. The latter bears, in season, numerous white flowers or yellow-green pods in a loose panicle. The leaves are rather suddenly narrowed at their tips. The petals are white, scarcely projecting from the sepals. The capsule is about ½ inch in length, robust, roundly triangular, and tipped with a blunt spine.

This species is locally abundant in the hammocks of the Everglade Keys, in the pine land and in the scrub-mangrove belt. It perches high in the hammock trees on exposed branches at the edges of hammocks always in full or nearly full sunshine. It is one of the last of the bromeliads to flower, beginning in late September.

MANY-FLOWERED CATOPSIS
Catopsis floribunda[1] (Brongn.) L. B. Smith (Fig. 29)

This is a fairly large plant with widely spreading, soft, drooping, translucent, grass-green leaves 10 to 16 inches in length. They are very wide at the base, then abruptly narrow and gradually taper to the tip. They are not glaucous as are those of the other two species of catopsis. The flower is a much-branched, drooping panicle, often 12

---

[1] *C. nutans* in Small's manual.

FIGURE 32. — Needle-leaved air plant. *Tillandsia setacea.*

to 24 inches long, bearing 25 to 50 flowers or capsules. The capsules are bluntly conical and about ½ inch long. The inconspicuous petals are white and scarcely protrude from the sepals.

This catopsis also is sparingly distributed through the Everglades Keys and the mangrove belt, always in deep shade and more numerous near the ground. The largest colonies are usually represented by relatively few plants. The tender leaves are eaten by deer, which may account to some extent for its scarcity. It blooms in late May and June.

SMALL CATOPSIS
Catopsis nutans (Sw.) Griseb. (Fig. D15)

This species is only about one-half the size of *floribunda* but it so closely resembles it that immature plants are easily confused. The leaves are somewhat duller, deep green above, glaucous beneath, and taper very gradually to a point. The flower stalk is rarely more than twelve inches in length, often unbranched and bears few, three to ten, blossoms or seed pods. The corolla is orange-yellow and widely spreading in sharp contrast to other native species.

This likewise is a shade-loving species found recently and rather sparingly in the Big Cypress swamp of Collier County. It blooms in September and October.

FIGURE D-14. — Yellow catopsis. *Catopsis berteroniana.* Plant (½ actual size) and seed pods (¹⁄₁₀ actual size). size).

GUZMANIA OR STRAP-LEAVED BROMELIAD
Guzmania monostachia (L.) Rusby (Fig. P15C)

This rather large air plant resembles typical wild-pines. The leaves, however, are limp and soft textured, widely spread, 12 to 24 inches long and droop at the tips. They are grass-green, glossy, with nearly parallel margins that suddenly narrow at the apex. The flower spike is ten to 15 inches long, stout, undivided and bears pink to salmon colored bracts that quickly wither and become membraneous. The milk-white petals are partly united into a club-shaped tube which is constricted by the shrinking of the calyx immediately after fertilization. The stamens have long strap-shaped filaments. The capsules are stout and cylindric, ½ to 1½ inches long with three shallow grooves.

This species is not widely distributed, but is very abundant locally in a few of the Everglades hammocks especially around Homestead. It grows on many kinds of trees but those plants which fall to the ground appear to be equally vigorous and often completely cover large areas of the soil. It blooms in late May through July, only a few flowers at a time, as the club-shaped pink to salmon colored spike pushes out through the rosette of leaves. It presents a most attractive sight when many of these spikes stand out like colored candles in the dimly lighted hammocks.

WILD-PINES
Tillandsia

Twelve species of the genus *Tillandsia* are recognized in Florida. All but one, *T. simulata*, occur in the southern portion of the state. Most species pattern a rather characteristic form consisting of a basal

FIGURE D-15. — Small catopsis. *Catopsis nutans*. Plant and fruiting spikes. (½ actual size).

rosette of leaves and a central flower spike. Spanish moss and ball moss are exceptions. The petals are not united and the corolla tube is concealed for most of its length by the sepals. The capsule is elongate and cylindrical.

The common name, wild pine, is applied for present purposes, to those species having leaves closely resembling the pineapple. Air plant is used for those with other types of leaves.

REFLEXED WILD PINE
Tillandsia balbisiana Schult (Fig. D16, P13C)

This species is readily recognized by its bulbous base formed by the sudden constriction of the leaves immediately above it, together with its very long, slenderly attenuate, recurved and twisted leaves. The leaves are sometimes 20 inches in length, grey-green to reddish and finely scurfy. The flower stalk is eight to 16 inches long, with simple terminally branched inflorescence. The bracts on the stem are long, slender, and recurved, green or often brilliant red. The petals are violet. The capsule is relatively long, 1¼ inches to two inches in length and somewhat triangular in cross section, bearing a small spine at the tip.

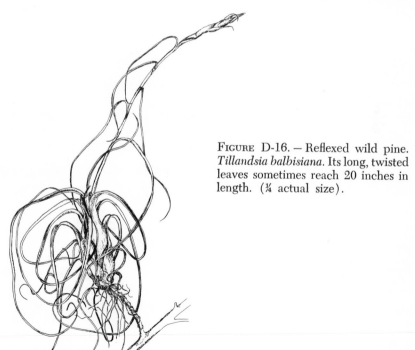

FIGURE D-16. — Reflexed wild pine. *Tillandsia balbisiana.* Its long, twisted leaves sometimes reach 20 inches in length. (¼ actual size).

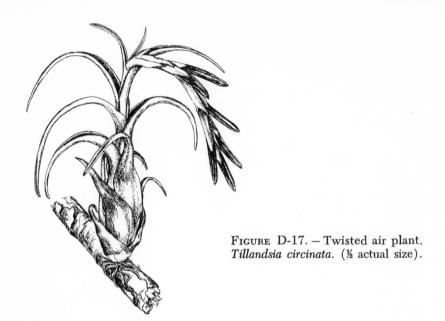

FIGURE D-17. — Twisted air plant.
Tillandsia circinata. (½ actual size).

This is a very abundant species throughout the area. It occurs in all situations and appears equally well adjusted to deep shade, where the leaves grow excessively long, or to bright sunlight where they are greatly contorted and highly colored. It grows on many trees including pine, and blooms sparingly through the winter months but abundantly from March to October.

TWISTED AIR PLANT
Tillandsia circinata Schlecht. (Fig. D17)

This is a small compact species four to eight inches tall and about the same width, growing in the open sunshine and, consequently, is beautifully colored with all shades from grey-green to blue-bronze or red. The plant body is short, bulbous at the base, (i.e. urn-shaped) with thick, strongly contorted, slenderly pointed quill-like leaves covered with minute grey scurfy scales. The flower spike is short, only two to four inches long, strongly curved, undivided, and pinkish in color, with closely appressed bracts and but few flowers. The petals are lavender. The capsules are 1¼ to 1½ inches long, three-grooved and somewhat triangular in cross section.

This abundant, beautifully colored, variably shaped and widely dispersed species adorns dead snags and the branches of shrubs and trees growing in the open, in all sites of southern Florida. Many individuals clump together, giving the old grey-bleached buttonwood and cypress snags a new usefulness and beauty. Flowers occur from mid-June through July and August.

STIFF-LEAVED WILD-PINE
Tillandsia fasciculata Sw. (Fig. D18, D19, D20; P13A)

This is our second largest species. It is a bulky plant with a wide-spreading base of stiff, gradually tapering grey-green leaves often 18 inches or more in length. Some leaves are longer than the flower stalk. The flower stalk is stout, stiffly erect, up to 20 inches tall, and provided with numerous green, cream-yellow, white or brilliant red bracts, usually bearing five to 12 elliptical, much flattened branchlets to form the spreading panicle. The flowers have violet petals. The capsule is about 1¼ inches long, stout, and triangular in cross section.

The stiff-leaved wild-pine is probably the most conspicuous and widely distributed species in south Florida. It shows tremendous variation in color of bracts, habit and size. When growing in deep shady hammocks its leaves may be as much as 40 inches long and strongly reflexed and twisted, resembling large plants of *T. balbisiana*. In the open it is compact and highly colored. It is one of the few species growing on the trunks of pines and cypress. Here the plants form large, burl-like protuberances that give a characteristic knobbiness to the tree trunks of the cypress sloughs. Flowers are borne from January through the summer.

A very attractive form with white petals and pale bracts occurs in the Flamingo area.

The compact flower spikes are often pierced by a small ambrosia beetle (*Xyleborus morstatti* Hopk.), which prevents the capsules from maturing.

T. hystricina Small is considered a variation of this species.

BANDED WILD-PINE
Tillandsia flexuosa Sw.[2] (Fig. D21, D22)

This plant is readily distinguished by its bulbous base and thick leaves, sometimes 16 inches in length, that bear characteristic alternating indefinite green and grey-green transverse bands. The leaves are strongly recurved and twisted. The flower stalk is slender, usually erect, 16 to 32 inches long, with bracts which do not overlap. The flowers are relatively few in a flattened widely branched panicle. They

---

[2]*T. aliofolia* in Small's manual.

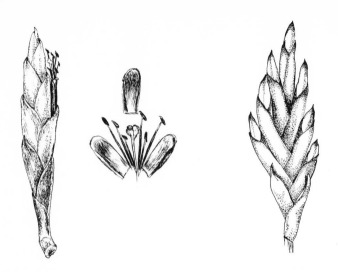

Figure D-18. — Stiff-leaved wild pine. *Tillandsia fasciculata*. Showing flower and spikelet. (natural size).

Figure D-19. — *T. fasciculata* seed pods. (natural size).

Figure D-20. — *T fasciculata* plant and flower spike. (⅙ actual size).

are set out at a wide angle to the ziz-zag stalk. The petals are pink. The capsule is 1½ to 2½ inches long and slightly stalked.

This is a widely distributed species in south Florida but never very abundant. It occurs in the mangrove belt, the Big Cypress, the Everglades Keys, and on Key Largo, usually in tops of trees in fairly sunny situations. It flowers in August and September.

REDDISH WILD-PINE
Tillandsia polystachia L. (Fig. 30, P13B)

This stiff-leaved species resembles *T. fasciculata* but has only about one half the complement of leaves and these are more slender, pointed, and erect. Neither the leaves nor the bracts exceed the length of the flower stalk. The bulbous base, suggesting *T. balbisiana* is only evident in older fruiting plants. The flower stalk is also more slender, but slightly branched, the flowers fewer than *T. fasciculata*. The capsule is 1¼ to 1½ inches in length and rather strongly triangular in cross section.

This species is locally abundant in the dwarf mangrove areas of the Park, on cypress trees in the sloughs of Dade, Monroe and Collier counties and the north end of Key Largo. It often grows in full sunshine, massed in great numbers on some trees. The erect form and highly colored reddish-grey leaves are very distinctive.

HOARY AIR PLANT
Tillandsia pruinosa Sw. (Fig. P15D)

This is a small, robust species only three to five inches tall with leaves swollen at the base to form a bulbous portion 1 to 1¼ inches in diameter bearing the short, compact and compressed flower stem. The entire plant is covered with dense silvery-scurfy pointed scales, giving it a silvery sheen with an undertone of dull cherry-green. The broad bases of the leaves are suddenly constricted into rather thick twisted tips up to four inches long with turned in edges.

The flower spike is contracted into an oval, flattened mass of pinkish bracts when flowering and bears two to five flowers. The petals are purple. The capsule is about one inch long, rather stout, sub-triangular in cross section, and beaked.

This small and attractive species has a strong resemblance to a huge spider with out-reaching hairy legs perched on the branches of the cypress or pond apple tree. The silvery-scaly covering suggests hoar frost, from which it received its Latin name. It is found rather sparingly in Collier County. It blooms in late fall and winter and probably to some extent throughout the year.

BALL MOSS, BUNCH MOSS
Tillandsia recurvata (L.) L. (Fig. 31)

This species has slender, quill-like recurved and twisted scurfy leaves ¾ to 1½ inches long, covered with silver green scales much like Spanish moss. However the stems are shortened so that the leaves arise more closely together than those of the Spanish moss and are interlocking at the base like a diminutive wild-pine. The stems, as they grow in length curl about their supports, entangling several plants together to give the characteristic ball-like appearance to the moss. One to four flowers terminate a slender, stiff, wire-like stalk two to six inches in length which bears bracts only at the base and tip. The petals are violet in color and the tips are strongly recurved. The stamens are not exserted, the capsules are 1 to 1¼ inches long, slender and spine tipped.

At first glance this species suggests a young plant of Spanish moss. In the bright winter sunshine the near leafless live-oaks appear from the distance to be covered with a silver sheen produced by the great

FIGURE 33. — Soft-leaved wild pine. *Tallandsia valenzuelana.*

66

numbers of these plants fastened in the topmost branches. This ubiquitous species prefers the exterior of tree canopies but accepts any support in the sunshine, even to wire fences and telephone wires. It is a wide ranging species throughout Florida and is found along the Gulf coast to Texas. It flowers in August and September.

NEEDLE-LEAVED AIR PLANT
Tillandsia setacea[3] Sw. (Fig. 32)

This dark green plant, often becoming reddish-bronze in the sunlight, forms into tuft-like rounded clumps, containing 20 to 50 individuals. These groups can be eight to 16 inches tall and nearly as wide. The needle-like leaves are four to 12 inches long, more slender than the flower-stalks, somewhat D-shaped in cross section, and dilated only at the extreme base. They are glabrous or scurfy only at the base. There are only ten to 20 leaves to a plant. The flower stalk is scurfy, very slender, nodding, about as long as the leaves and bears a few very attenuate bracts, the topmost rarely exceeding the spike. One to four flowers are grouped at the apex. The petals are lavender, the capsule is ¾ to 1¼ inches long and beaked.

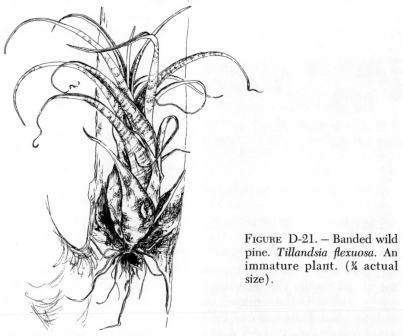

FIGURE D-21. — Banded wild pine. *Tillandsia flexuosa*. An immature plant. (¼ actual size).

---

[3]*T. tenuifolia* in Small's manual.

The needle-leaved air plant — its leaves somewhat resembling pine-needles — is abundant and widely dispersed. Its range extends north into Georgia. Often it nearly covers the branches and trunks of oaks and many other trees, giving them a fuzzy, indefinite outline. When in the open, in considerable sunlight, the leaves take on a beautiful coppery-red or bronze color. It flowers in early August and September.

SLENDER-LEAVED WILD PINE
Tillandsia simulata Small (Fig. P14B)

A plant intermediate in size between *Tillandsia fasciulata* and *T. tenuifolia*. The plants occur singly or in small clumps in which each plant is readily distinct. The leaves have a very short broadened base as in *T. tenuifolia* but are much longer, more numerous, up to 50 per plant, and deeply cupped for more than half the length as in *T. fasci-culata*. They differ from the latter in being much more slender. The leaves and very slender bracts of this species are as long or usually exceed the spike. They are scurfy throughout their length. The flower stalk is simple or feebly branched and bears from three to ten flowers. The petals are blue.

This species occurs in central peninsular Florida associated with *T. fasciculata* and *T. tenuifolia* but has not been observed in the Everglades Park. It grows commonly on cypress and other trees in moist hammocks.

SPANISH MOSS
Tillandsia usneoides L. (Fig. P13D, D23)

This plant droops from its support in long, gray festoons. The slender stem is greatly elongated, twining, and covered with silvery scales. It is about $\frac{1}{25}$ inch in diameter and 20 to 50 inches long, bearing at intervals numerous short leaves, round in cross section and 1 to $2\frac{1}{2}$ inches in length.

The tiny inconspicuous flowers are fragrant, and occur singly, on a very short stalk in the axils of leaves on younger portions of the plant. The petals are yellowish-green with strongly recurved tips. Two long bracts of unequal length extend considerably beyond the flower. The capsules are $\frac{1}{2}$ to 1 inch long and spine tipped.

Spanish moss is one of the most characteristic natural features of the coastal South. The drooping festoons which cover the live oaks, cypress, and in fact any support, arrest the attention of visitor as does no other plant. During storms the waving and weaving of these plants give the impression that the giant oaks and sturdy cypresses are themselves moving with the wind. This plant is the basis of much legend and

FIGURE D-22. — Banded wild pine. *Tillandsia flexuosa.* Tip of spike showing zig-zag rachis and pods. (½ actual size).

lore in the South. It has many common names, among them long-moss, Florida-moss, wood-crape and crape-moss.

Spanish moss is commonly used as a mulch around plants and the fibrous interior of the stems called "vegetable hair" provides stuffing for mattresses and furniture. At one time collecting and preparing of this moss for industrial uses was a two million dollar industry in the state of Florida (Shoemaker 1958). In pecan groves it becomes a nuisance and is expensive to remove from the trees.

It occurs throughout Florida including the upper Florida Keys and along the coast from Virginia to Texas. In extreme southern Florida its distribution is very localized. Dr. W. B. Robertson has suggested this might be explained in part by its use in the nests of some birds particularly that of the swallow-tailed kite. Perhaps the drier winters in this area restrict its natural spread but once established it covers its host with characteristic festoons. It flowers in April to June and sparingly throughout the summer.

GIANT WILD-PINE
Tillandsia utriculata L. (Fig. D24, D25)

This commanding species, our largest air plant, has a spread up to 48 inches. Its leaves are pale green, very wide at the base, gradually tapering to a point, and often 24 inches or more in length. They diverge gracefully from the base and arch to give a broad cornucopia-like form. The much-branched and many-flowered stalk is erect, often over 70 inches tall. The stem is not completely concealed by the bracts and the flower-bearing rachises are zig-zag. The petals are cream colored to ivory white, projecting about the length of the bracts. The capsules are 1¾ to 2½ inches long and closely appressed to the stem.

The giant wild-pine is widely distributed throughout the area and is a very conspicuous feature in some of the hammocks of the Everglades Keys. It is decidedly more abundant in open stands of the mangrove belt where it is commonly seen, perched on buttonwoods. It blooms in late May and June, a few flowers at a time, the lowest flower on the lowest branches of the panicle opening first. Thus the flowering period of an individual plant is spread over two or three weeks. This species does not produce secondary plants from basal buds as do many of its relatives. Thus it is always found as a single plant.

SOFT-LEAVED WILD PINE
Tillandsia valenzuelana A. Rich. (Fig. 33)

This species has drooping leaves eight to 20 inches in length which spreads out in a widely curved arch from the base of the plant. Individual leaves are fairly narrow, rather strongly cupped, are gradually tapered and covered with a silvery bloom. They have a soft texture and are very brittle and snap off cleanly on bending, in contrast with the stiff, tough leaves of most air plants. The flower spike

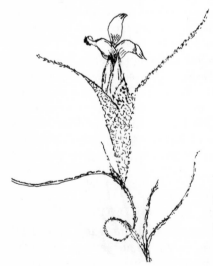

FIGURE D-23. — Spanish moss. *Tillandsia usneoides*. This tiny flower occurs singly on a short stalk in the axils of leaves. (natural size).

70

is slender, usually curved or drooping, up to 24 inches long, simple or branched, with rather short, closely appressed, blunt bracts. The petals are lavender. The capsules are ¾ to 1¾ inches long, somewhat triangular in cross section.

This very attractive, silvery-grey, shade-loving form is locally abundant throughout the Everglades Keys and cypress swamps, but less common in the mangrove forests. It is a low-growing plant and seldom found high on the trunks. It blooms from late July through September.

FIGURE D-24. — Giant wild pine. *Tillandsia utriculata.* Portion of stem to show that bracts do not completely cover the internode as in most native bromeliads. (natural size).

FIGURE D-25. — *T. utriculata* showing seed pods on the zig-zag rachis. (½ actual size).

FIGURE 34. — *Bulbophyllum pachyrhachis*. Plant and flower spike

Orchids
Family Orchidaceae

The orchids comprise one of the largest families of plants. Over twenty thousand species have been found and described throughout the world. These show a tremendous variation in size, habit of growth, and especially in diversity of floral structures. Many of the orchids of Florida are terrestrial but in the tropics they are predominantly epiphytic. None is known to be parasitic (Correll, 1950).

Practically all orchids are perennials and many grow so slowly that they require several years to mature and produce flowers. Most of them enlarge and produce new plants vegetatively, that is, from buds which form along the rootstalk or stem. Great masses of plants are thus formed from an original seedling. Sometimes, as in the case of the cow-horn orchid, the whole assemblage that forms from one original seed may weigh nearly 75 pounds, or in the case of creeping types, large surfaces of trees, limbs and trunk may be completely covered.

In spite of their prolific seed production and distribution by wind, many species of orchids are relatively rare and very restricted in their occurrence. Often only a few flowers become fertilized and produce pods or viable seeds. In some species, after one flower is fertilized, the others fail to develop, while in other species, the spikes keep on producing a profusion of flowers. The soft, succulent flower pedicels and stalks are often eaten by cutworms, grasshoppers or snails, while the larger types, such as some oncidiums, are relished by deer. The pseudobulbs are frequently gnawed by rodents, possibly to obtain water from the succulent pulp during dry periods.

In southern Florida one hammock may have many species while another may have only the ubiquitous ones such as the butterfly orchid or the night-blooming epidendron. Local fires, as mentioned earlier, probably play the most important role in this erratic distribution. Another condition which contributes to the scarcity of certain orchid species is that the seeds of some will not germinate without the assistance of certain fungi (Ames, 1947).

Other species are associated with fungi in a still different manner. In this case the fungus forms a fuzzy coating around the roots and furnishes certain nutrients to the plants. The fungi that lives in this relationship with the plant roots are known as mycorrhiza. Another explanation for this local distribution of rarer orchids may be that the seeds of such species have but recently drifted into the area from the tropics. If this is true the more recent migrants would naturally be restricted to smaller areas near points of establishment. Every few years what appears to be a new migrant is found in southern Florida.

Formerly roots or bulbs of many kinds of orchids were used for medicinal purposes, especially among the African peoples. It is thought that some of the African species now found in the West Indies were brought over by slaves and grown for their medicinal value. A tea, known as Faham tea, is made from the roots of one African species. The American Indians used a few native species medicinally. The pseudo-bulb of the butterfly orchid was eaten as food and that of the cow-horn orchid was used for an adhesive. Of course vanilla, also produced from an orchid, is familiar to everyone.

The culture and sale of orchids has become big business. Millions of dollars are invested in the commercial growing and sale of these plants. Thousands of enthusiastic amateurs have adopted orchid growing as a hobby. However, the culture of orchids is a highly specialized procedure, and elaborate techniques have been devised to germinate the seeds and secure new plants. The reader is referred to the numerous publications on this industry; among them Burnett (1958), Noble (1960), Hawkes (1947, 1961).

The demands of amateurs for building up a collection of native orchids has put a high price on rarer ones and greatly accelerated the disappearance of these species from the Everglades National Park and from the cypress swamps of Collier County. Some forms that were relatively common ten years ago are now extremely rare, or possibly extinct. The effort of the Park administration to protect rare and vanishing species is rendered extremely difficult by the lack of ranger personnel and also by the fact that much land within the Park boundaries is still privately owned.

A unique feature of many orchids is the specialization of their flowers so as to insure cross fertilization by insects. These modifications involve the lip and the column, and the arrangement is such that an insect can enter only along a certain route, therefore, any pollen it may be carrying will be certain to come in contact with the stigma. Also as the insect leaves, pollen from the same flower is rubbed off onto the body of the insect to be carried elsewhere.

The diverse and remarkable specialization of the floral structures for pollination so intrigued Charles Darwin that he made extensive observations which he published in a book entitled *Various Contrivances by which Orchids are Fertilized by Insects* (Darwin 1877).

Mrs. Mary Francis Baker in her charming little book *Florida Wild Flowers* (1949) introduces her discussion of the native orchids as follows:

> "The very word orchid calls up suggestions of grace and of grotesqueness, of strange beauty and of uncanny mimicry. More than any other family of flowering plants the orchids seem to have developed inexplicably along lines of their own. In extravagant variety of form the flowers rival all others; their adaptations for cross-pollination are many and marvelous, and some remain open for many weeks; they clothe themselves in the dullest colors, or open in gay and brilliant beauty, and in odor they range from the abattoir to the Elysian Fields."

Because of the great modification of structure in orchid flowers, it is often difficult for the amateur to recognize the usual floral parts of other plants. To help understand this specialization one of the larger orchid flowers is illustrated somewhat diagrammatically (Fig. D26). The three sepals and two of the petals are seen to be not too greatly different from some other flowers. However, the third petal has been so much enlarged that in many orchids it is the most conspicuous structure of the whole flower. This is called the lip. It appears in many fantastic shapes, often three-lobed. In the vanillas it is tubular. The stamens and pistils of orchid flowers have become fused together, forming an odd structure termed the column. It is difficult to recognize this column in orchids as the counterpart of the conspicuous and often attractive stamens and pistil of an ordinary flower. The tip of the column bears one, two, or rarely three pollen masses (pollinia) and often a structure that secretes a sticky fluid, supposedly to insure the adherence of the pollen grains brought in by a visiting insect.

The flower is borne on a pedicel which is actually, in part, the immature seed pod or capsule. This latter is one-celled. The pod develops rapidly immediately after fertilization into many varied shapes. Ultimately these pods split longitudinally to free the dust-like, powdery seeds. In the case of some of the vanilla orchids, seeds are much larger, hard, round, and are suspended in a sticky matrix. When ripe, this oozes out of the pods carrying the seeds. These pods or capsules afford reliable characters for identification and recognition of the species. They are usually present on the plant for several months before the seeds finally mature.

The vegetative structures of the orchids are likewise specialized but in contrast with the flowers, modifications are toward simplification. Many of the epiphytic orchids develop a basal swelling or pseudobulb, which is a modification of the stem. One to several leaves may be borne on the apex of this structure.

Flower stalks may originate either from the top or from the base of the pseudobulb or rhizome. In other forms the flowers may develop at the apex of a leafy stem, or from the axil of a leaf. Such variations are helpful in recognizing the plant.

Key to the Epiphytic Orchids

As an aid to identifying our epiphytic orchids, it is practical to think of them as forming three distinct types: (a) the vine-like types or vanillas; (b) the leafless species, and (c) those bearing leaves. These are characterized as follows:

1. Climbing vines having green, yellowish or brownish,
    thick rope-like jointed stems, and aerial roots
    arising from the nodes; leaves present or absent .... Vanillas
    Plants not vine-like 2
2. Leafless plants composed of a mass of clinging,
    grayish-green, compressed roots, flowers
    spurred .... Leafless epiphytic orchids
3. Plants with stems and leaves, and not vine-like .... Leafly epiphytic orchids

Key to the Leafy Orchids

1. Plants without pseudobulbs or pseudobulbs
    indistinct 2
    Plants with pseudobulbs distinct 14
2. Stems bearing only one leaf 3
    Stems bearing two or more leaves 4
3. Plants small, 1½ to 3½ inches tall .... Lepanthopsis
    Plants large, 6 to 20 inches tall .... Pleurothalis
4. Flowers borne singly at base of plant, scarcely
    protruding from axile of leaves; leaves
    sheathing one another at base .... Maxillaria
    Flowers borne on a stalk 5
5. Flower stalk at tip of the leafy portion of stem 6
    Flower stalk separate, arising from base of
    plants, not leafy 12
6. Flower stalk with distinct leafless and bractless
    portion between leafy stem and flowers 7
    Flower stalk short, at end of leafy stem, largely
    concealed by bracts 9

76

16. Leaves over 12 inches long, thin, linear,

16. Leaves over 12 inches long, thin, linear,
    several from top of bulb and rhizome 17

    Leaves shorter, thick, leathery, one or two
    from top of bulb 18

17. Bulb elongate fusiform, often over 6
    inches long ....Cow-horn orchid
                                                    Cyrtopodium

    Bulb oblong, ovoid, strongly compressed ....Florida oncidium
                                                    O. floridanum

18. Bulb pyramidal, five-angled, robust, bearing
    two leaves ....*Bulbophyllum*

    Bulb fusiform, slender, bearing one leaf ....Trinidad macradenia
                                                    Macradenia

    Bulb long tapering, strongly compressed,
    bearing 2 or 3 leaves from apex ....Spider orchid
                                                    Brassia

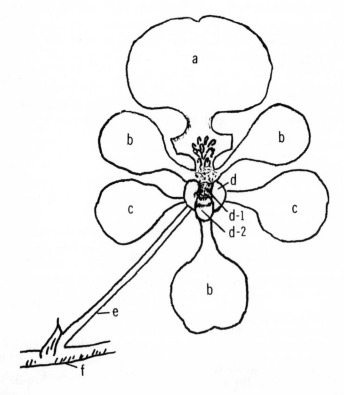

FIGURE D-26. — Diagrammatic sketch of an orchid flower to show structure.
a — lip; b — sepals; c — petals; d — column bearing stigmatic surface (d-1)
and anther (d-2); e — ovary and pedicel; f — stem and bract.

SPIDER ORCHID
Brassia caudata (L.) Lindl. (Fig. P19A)

A fairly large plant usually 15 to 20 inches in length, having large flattened pseudobulbs two to four inches long that narrow toward the apex. The leaves are dark green, broadly-linear, flexible eight to 13 inches long, ¾ to 1¼ inches wide, two or three arising from the top of the bulb. The unbranched flower stalk arises from a sheathing bract at the base of the bulb and is 15 to 20 inches long. The flowers are large and showy, greenish-yellow, spotted with brown, having the two lateral sepals long-acuminate up to four inches in length and shorter lanceolate petals. The capsule is somewhat ellipsoidal, three-ribbed, beaked at both ends, and 1½ to 2 inches long.

This strikingly beautiful orchid is a rarity in the region and it may be on its way to extinction in southern Florida. The plant, except when in flower, is so similar to the very common shell orchid that it can be recognized only on close examination. This confusion may be a safeguard. The leaves are softer, glossier and more suddenly constricted at the tip than those of the shell orchid, and the flower stalk arises from the base of the bulb instead of the tip. It grows in damp, dark hammocks, either on the ground or on fallen tree trunks. None has been seen on higher branches, but in that position it could be recognized only when in bloom. It flowers in May and June.

BULBOPHYLLUM
Bulbophyllum pachyrachis (A. Rich.) Griseb. (Fig. 34)

A rather small plant from four to six inches tall having pseudobulbs arising along a somewhat woody rhizome. The bulbs are robust, somewhat pyramidal, ½ inch to 1¼ inches in length, five-angled and deeply fluted. The two leaves arising from the apex of the bulb, are stiff and leathery, from two to four inches in length, and ½ to ¾ inches wide, linear with rounded tips. The flower stalk is a pendent, fleshy, club-shaped spike, three to four inches long, arising from the base of the bulb.

The small flowers, less than ¼ inch long, are set in cup-like depressions at the base of a triangular bract ⅛ inch long. The stem of the spike and the flowers are yellowish-green marked with numerous purple spots. The sepals are boat-shaped, the tips recurved, the lip and petals more slender, creamy white at the base and purplish-speckled toward the tips.

This orchid was found by Fred Fuchs, Jr. of Naranja, Florida, growing on pond apple trees in Collier County. It is a recent discovery and apparently not common in Florida. Flowers have been observed in November and December.

LEAFLESS EPIPHYTIC ORCHIDS

The following three orchids can be treated as a group for present purposes. They are small leafless plants whose roots have taken over the photosynthetic function of the leaves and form the most conspicuous part of the plant. These are grey-green, provided with chlorophyll, and form a network twining over and around the support. The roots may extend ten to twenty inches along this support to which they adhere tightly.

Key to the Leafless Orchids

1. Roots less than ⅟₂₅ inch wide, raceme with
   few flowers or pods ....*Harrisella*
   Roots ⅛ to ¼ inch wide 2
2. Spikes with many flowers or pods; these
   very small, two-ranked ....*Campylocentrum*
   Spikes one-flowered; flower large and showy,
   lip deeply bifid; pod 2 to 3 inches
   long, slender ....Ghost orchid
   Polyrrhiza

CAMPYLOCENTRUM

Campylocentrum pachyrrhizum (Reichb, f.) Rolfe (Fig. D27, P16C)

A small leafless plant with clusters of dark green flattened roots about ¼ inch wide, radiating from a center at which point several short many-flowered spikes, 1 to 1½ inches long may arise. The flowers are greenish-yellow, small, about ¼ inch long, numerous, and crowded in two ranks on the short spikes. The lip is produced at the base into a small sac-like spur. The capsules are hairy, about ¼ inch long and bear five or six ribs. They are closely set in two ranks along the slender stalk, which bears numerous bracts.

This species occurs in Collier County on various hardwood stems. It flowers in the late winter.

FIGURE D-27. — Campylocentrum. *Camplyocentrum pachyrrhizum.* Seed pods clusted in two rows on the short spikes. (2 times actual size).

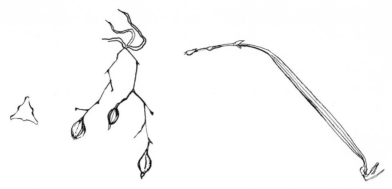

FIGURE D-28. – Harrisella. *Harrise-* FIGURE D-29. – Ghost orchid. *Pol-*
lla porrecta. Seed pods. (natural *yrrhiza lindenii.* Seed pods.
size).

HARRISELLA
Harrisella porrecta (Reichb, f.) Fawc. & Rendle (Fig. D28)

This species has very narrow grey-green roots scarcely ⅟₂₅ inch wide. The flowers are few about ⅛ inch broad, greenish-yellow, the lip is boat shaped, having its apex abruptly beaked and its base bearing a globular spur, which often persists on the apex of the capsule. The flower stalks are 1 to 1½ inches long and bear stalked subglobular, strongly six-ribbed capsules about ¼ inch long, grouped at the apex.

This, our smallest epiphytic orchid, is more common in the central portions of the state, but extends southward into Collier County. It occurs on many broad-leafed and coniferous trees, especially citrus and juniper. Flowers appear in the late summer.

GHOST ORCHID, PALM-POLLY, WHITE BUTTERFLY ORCHID
Polyrrhiza lindenii (Lindl.) Cogn. (Fig. D29, P16A)

This species is intermediate between the two preceding in size of the aerial roots which are less than ¼ inch in diameter, but very long and tortuous, like *Campylocentrum.* The flowers are fragrant, large, 1 to 1½ inches broad, showy, white, with the petals and sepals widely spreading. The lip is somewhat three-lobed, the central lobe extended into two long slender projections two to three inches in length and curved to resemble a pair of ram's horns. The base of the lip is prolonged into a slender spur three to five inches long. The capsule is slender, from two to four inches in length and about ¼ inch in diameter, borne on a bracted stalk four to eight inches long.

The strikingly beautiful flower of this orchid has been likened by Correll to a "snow-white frog suspended in mid-air". It is indeed an unusual surprise to come across such a showy bloom in the deep shaded woods where it occurs. It is found in the cypress sloughs of Collier and Dade Counties, principally on pop-ash (*Fraxinus*) but also on pond-apple and cypress trees.

COW HORN ORCHID, CIGAR ORCHID
Cyrtopodium punctatum (L.) Lindl. (Fig. 35, 36, D30, P14A)

A very large orchid, the aggregate of plants sometimes weighing over 75 pounds, composed of numerous fusiform "cigar-shaped" pseudobulbs four to 12 inches long and ½ to 1½ inches in diameter, ringed with numerous leaf scars. The younger pseudobulbs bear several long, linear, plicate leaves 12 to 24 inches in length, with drooping tips. Numerous slender erect aerial roots, two to six inches tall, surround the base. The flower stalk is up to five feet long spreading into a broad panicle of yellow, madder to brown, spotted, frilled flowers about 1½ inches wide. The sepals and petals are slightly stalked and frilled; the lip is broadly three-lobed, mid lobe wider than long, with the margin frilled and beaded. The drooping capsule is about three inches long and 1 to 1½ inches thick.

This, our largest and possibly the most arresting orchid of the area, was at one time very common but is now becoming rare because it is so much in demand by orchid growers and collectors. It is most abundant on dead buttonwoods around open glades of the mangrove areas. It also occurs in some hammocks of Long Pine Key and in the Big Cypress sloughs. It prefers much light and is best developed on the upper parts of large trees. Many plants fall to the ground, and may do very well in sunny places but in deeper shade, gradually decline. In dry seasons, the watery bulbs are eaten by mammals. They have a mucilaginous pulp which the Indians and early settlers used for glue. Flowers appear in March and April.

This orchid does well in cultivation and is easily propagated from seed. Seeds that were shed over some old coconut hulls lying on the ground in a propagating house at Pine Island, Everglades National Park, germinated and produced hundreds of seedlings. These grew to be two to six inches tall by the second season.

BROWN EPIDENDRUM
Epidendrum anceps Jacq. (Fig. D31, P18B)

A rather tall, leafy plant with numerous upright stems 24 to 30 inches in height, each bearing eight to 12 elongate to elliptic glossy and rigid leaves, two to six inches long and ½ to 1½ inches wide,

FIGURE D-30. — Cowhorn orchid. *Cyrtopodium punctatum*. Cigar-shaped pseudobulbs bearing several long, linear, plicate leaves, with drooping tips. (⅓ actual size).

FIGURE 35. — Cow-horn orchid. *Cyrtopodium punctatum.* Showing pods.

FIGURE 36. — Cow-horn orchid. *Cyrtopodium punctatum.* Showing flowers.

with clasping petioles that conceal the flattened stem. There are no pseudobulbs. The flowers are in a compact globular head terminating a compressed, keeled peduncle which is an extension of the leafy stem. This peduncle is practically concealed by brown scarious bracts. The flowers are small, about ½ inch broad, greenish brown to tawny, having sepals and petals of about equal length, the former oblique, the latter, spatulate. The lip is broadly three-lobed, the middle lobe notched. The capsule is ovoid, about ¾ inch long.

This is a widely distributed species in south Florida, particularly abundant in the Big Cypress swamp and in some of the Everglades Keys. It forms large clumps and is sometimes terrestrial. Flowers appear throughout the year but chiefly in the fall.

DOLLAR ORCHID
Epidendrum boothianum[1] Lindl. (Fig. P17B)

A medium-sized plant up to 12 inches tall forming dense clumps of round strongly flattened pseudobulbs, which bear two, but rarely three, dark green, rigid, oblanceolate and slightly twisted leaves two to six inches long, and ½ to 1 inch wide. The flower stalks, four to ten inches long, arise from a prominent sheath on top of the bulb and carry a loose, simple raceme of two to eight flowers. The flowers are ½ to ¾ inch broad, with the sepals and petals quite similar, widely spreading, yellow with many brown-to-purple spots; the lip is greenish yellow, somewhat four-sided in outline. The capsule is strongly three-winged, ovoid, stalked and pendent, ¾ to 1 inch long and half as wide.

This orchid is distinctive both in the color of the flower and shape of the pseudobulb. It occurs sparingly in southern Florida being most common along the coast of the Cape Sable and Flamingo areas, and on Key Largo. It is found chiefly on buttonwood. Formerly it was much more abundant than at present. It is in demand by collectors. The severe freeze of 1956 destroyed many clumps in the Flamingo area, and the hurricane Donna destroyed many more in 1960. It blooms in September through early winter.

---

[1] The conservative interpretation of the genus *Epidendrum* has been followed in this book. On the other hand, Dressler (Brittonia 13(3): 253-266, 1961) has reconsidered the genus *Encyclia* and has changed several species treated here to this genus. The species that have been changed to *Encyclia* are: *E. boothiana, E. cochleata, E. pygmaea.* Probably further study will indicate that *Epidendrum tampense* should be transferred to this genus. This would be in accordance with Small's treatment of this species. —M. R. Birdsey.

CLAM-SHELL ORCHID
Epidendrum cochleatum L. (Fig. D32, P19B)

A fairly large glabrous plant ten to 20 inches tall which often forms large clumps. The prominent pseudobulbs are three to four inches long and ½ to ¾ inch wide, strongly compressed and tapering toward the apex where they carry one to three elongate linear leaves six to 15 inches in length and ½ to 1½ inches in width. These are thin with long tapering and drooping tips. The raceme carrying several flowers originates from the tip of the bulb between the leaves. The flowers are showy, from 1½ to 2 inches wide with spreading, yellow-green tapering sepals and petals; the lip is purple with darker veins and spots, ¾ to one inch wide and broadly clam-shell shaped. The capsule is ellipsoidal, up to two inches long, strongly three winged, stalked and pendent.

This showy orchid is widely distributed and abundant throughout southern Florida except in the Florida Keys. It usually occurs in moist shaded situations on the branches and trunks of many kinds of trees. It also is found frequently growing on logs and on the ground. It blooms throughout the year but more abundantly in late summer and fall.

The Florida plants have been given the varietal name *triandra* by Ames because of the three anthers. The West Indian plants have but one anther (Correll 1950).

GREEN-FLY ORCHID, TREE ORCHID
Epidendrum conopseum R. Br. (Fig. P14D)

A small epiphytic plant with numerous ascending stems eight to 16 inches tall bearing two to four oblong, rather stiff and twisted, leaves, their bases partly clasping the stem. There are no pseudobulbs. The flowers are grouped at the apex of a slender peduncle. They are about ¾ inch wide, greenish-lemon tinged with purple, having slender, spatulate, widely spreading sepals and petals; the lip is broadly three lobed. The capsule is drooping, ovoid, subtriangular, beaked, six-keeled, ½ to 1 inch long and about ¼ inch wide.

This is one of the most wide spread epiphytes of the southeast, extending from central Florida into North Carolina and west to Louisiana along the coast but it has not been found within the region here treated. Correll (1950) states that it is the only epiphytic orchid of North America occurring outside Florida. It is often found growing among epiphytic ferns and air plants and thus difficult to see. It grows on a variety of hosts and flowers appear throughout the year. They are fragrant especially at night.

UMBELLED EPIDENDRUM
Epidendrum difforme Jacq. (Fig. 37, D33)

A medium-sized, matted, creeping plant with numerous, sprawling or pendent stems, two to six inches in length and bearing up to eight or ten leaves with clasping bases that practically conceal the stem Pseudobulbs are lacking. The leaves are thick, fleshy, rigid, elongate-oval, two-ranked, 1½ to four inches in length, and ½ to 1½ inches wide, often slightly notched at the tip. The flowers are pendent on long, slender pedicels at the apex of the leafy stem. They are pale green, ½ to one inch wide; the sepals and petals are broadly spreading, spatulate, and somewhat similar in shape; the lip is broadly kidney-shaped, often three-lobed, and the middle lobe distinctly notched. The capsule is pendent on a long peduncle, globose, slightly beaked, and about ¾ inch long.

This species is more common in the sloughs of the Big Cypress country in the western part of the area, but is occasionally found in oak hammocks of Dade County and rarely in the mangrove forests. It is local in distribution, but often plentiful where it does occur, usually in deep shade. It blooms chiefly in the fall and winter.

NIGHT-BLOOMING EPIDENDRUM
Epidendrum nocturnum Jacq. (Fig. D34, P16D)

One of our larger orchids, having erect, long, leafy, compressed stems, up to 30 inches in length, forming at times large clumps of 25 to 30 stalks. There are no pseudobulbs. Long, conspicuous flattened grey-green roots extend over the support from the base of these clumps. The leaves are oblong to elliptic, from three to six inches long and ½ to 1½ inches wide, being larger toward the tip of the stem, stiff, widely spaced, somewhat two-ranked, the bases sheathing the stem.

The flowers are few, one to five on a very short, zig-zag raceme at the apex of the leafy stem. Usually but one flower blooms at a time. This is large and showy, over two inches wide, borne on a long slender peduncle two to four inches in length with widely spreading linear sepals and petals 1½ to 2 inches long, the former are a greenish-white and broader, the latter white. The lip is white, three-lobed, the mid-lobe long, filiform, and yellowish, the lateral lobes resembling a pair of wings. The capsule is pendent, fusiform, beaked, widest near the tip, 1½ to two inches long.

This orchid is readily recognized by its white spider-like and highly fragrant flowers borne at the tip of the leafy stem. It is widely

FIGURE D-31. — Brown epidendrum. *Epidendrum anceps.* Flowers terminating a penduncle which is an extension of the leafy stem. (¼ actual size).

distributed in southern Florida except in the Florida Keys, and is common to all plant associations and on many host trees. It flowers throughout the year. The flowers are much more fragrant at night, and fade very quickly in contrast to those of many species.

DWARF EPIDENDRUM
Epidendrum pygmaeum Hook. (Fig. 38)

A very small, creeping plant, sending up numerous slender, fusiform pseudobulbs, less than ¼ inch wide and ¾ to 1½ inches long, from scaly, much branched rhizomes supported by long white, conspicuous roots. There are usually two sessile leaves on the apex of the bulb. These are widely spreading, stiff, widest at the middle, ¾ to two inches long, and ⅜ to ¾ inch wide, shiny and finely ribbed on the back. One to three small, greenish white flowers tinged with purple are set deep in the axil of the leaves. The sepals are broad, the petals are narrow and both abruptly acuminate; the lip is broad with a purplish spot at the apex. The capsule is almost sessile, subglobular, about ⅜ inch in length, and strongly winged.

This, one of our smaller orchids, grows near the ground in shaded places in the cypress sloughs of Monroe and Collier Counties. It is not common, and blooms in February and March.

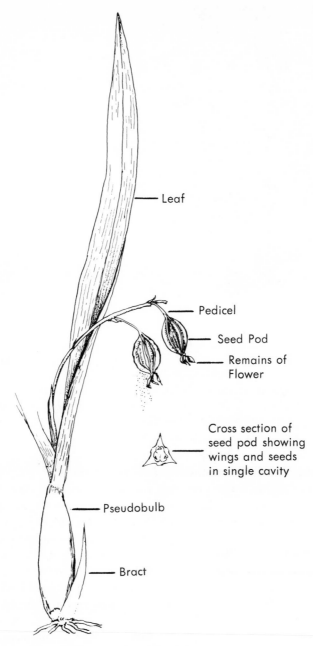

Leaf

Pedicel

Seed Pod

Remains of
Flower

Cross section of
seed pod showing
wings and seeds
in single cavity

Pseudobulb

Bract

FIGURE D-32. — Clam shell orchid. *Epidendrum cochleatum.* Pseudobulb,
leaf and seed pods. (½ actual size).

FIGURE 37. — Umbelled epidendrum. *Epidendrum difforme*. Plant in flower.

MATTED EPIDENDRUM
Epidendrum rigidum Jacq. (Fig. 39, D35)

A scraggly, creeping, matted plant forming immense colonies often covering the limbs and trunks of its host, having numerous short stems concealed by persistent leaf sheafs and bearing two-ranked stiff, oblong leaves, ¾ to 4 inches long and ¼ to ¾ inch wide, rounded or notched at the tip. There are no pseudobulbs.

The rather small, greenish-white flowers are about ⅜ inch wide, and are borne on a slender, zig-zag, compressed spike arising from the tip of the leafy stem; they are partially concealed by the large green triangular and clasping bracts. The sepals and petals are widely spreading, about ⅕ inch long, the latter more slender than the former. The capsule is broadly oval, sessile, beaked, partly concealed by a bract and usually less than ½ inch long.

This orchid is anything but beautiful when compared with its neighbors, but the great masses of matted green which covers the trunks and branches of the hammock trees in the Everglades Keys rank it as one of the most vigorous. Correll terms it "an epiphytic weed". It is widely distributed in the area on many hosts. Flowers can be found at all seasons. The plant prefers shady situations.

FIGURE 38. — Dwarf epidendrum. *Epidendrum pygmaeum*. Plant in flower.

FIGURE 39. — Matted epidendrum. *Epidendrum rigidum*. Plant bearing pods.

STROBILIFERUM
Epidendrum strobiliferum Reichb. f. (Fig. 40, D36)

A rather small, matted epiphyte with creeping, much-branched, scaly stems that root frequently and send up numerous shoots bearing two to ten leaves; the latter are ½ to 2 inches long, greenish-purple, stiff, widest at the base and tapering to the slightly notched tip, and set at nearly right angles to the stem. The few flowered racemes arise from the tip of the branches and bear relatively large-ribbed bracts that nearly conceal the flowers and, later, much of the capsule. The flowers are very small, about ¼ inch wide, white or yellowish, with the segments faintly ribbed. The capsule is subglobular, less than ¼ inch long.

This inconspicuous orchid is found in the cypress sloughs of Collier and Lee Counties, but has not been found in the eastern areas of the Park. It is not common but is found occasionally on smooth-barked trees, particularly ash and bay. It flowers in March and April.

BUTTERFLY ORCHID
Epidendrum tampense Lindl. (Fig. D37, P14C)

A medium-to-large plant, having one to three stiff, linear leaves three to 12 inches long and ½ to one inch wide, arising from the top of a pear-shaped bulb, which is occasionally as much as three inches long, grayish-green, often touched with purple.

Few to many flowers occur in a loose raceme terminating a long, slender stalk arising from the tip of the bulb. The flowers are 1¼ to 1¾ inches broad, showy, fragrant, with the sepals and petals somewhat oblanceolate, greenish-yellow and striped or spotted with magenta. The lip is usually white or yellowish-white, deeply three-lobed, the middle one orbicular with several magenta stripes which usually fuse at their bases. The capsule is slightly beaked, ellipsoidal, one to two inches long, bearing six flat ridges.

This distinctive, attractive, and abundant orchid is the most common and widely distributed in the area. It sems to thrive everywhere, on the shrubs of the glades, on the dead snags of the mangroves, or in the deep shade of the oak hammocks and cypress sloughs. It is one of the few orchids growing in the Florida Keys. It may appear as a tiny bulb, one leaf and one or two attractive flowers, or as a great mass of bulbs and leaves, forming burl-like knobs on the side of the tree host. In the deep shade the leaves are long and slender and the bulbs may be three inches in length. Any support suits this ubiquitous epiphyte and where trees are scarce the oolitic outcrops of the glades or the pinelands suffice. It grows well in sunlight and flowers all year, especially from March to June. The flowers vary greatly in color; albino and reddish forms are not uncommon.

IONOPSIS
Ionopsis utricularioides (Sw.) Lindl. (Fig. P17D)

A medium-sized plant, four to 15 inches tall, with short, stout, leafy stems arising from a creeping rootstalk and a very small and inconspicuous pseudobulb usually hidden between the leaves. The leaves vary from four to ten per stem, are stiff, thick, linear, four to eight inches long and ¼ to ¾ inch wide, usually purplish, ribbed, slightly cupped and sharply tipped. The inflorescence forms a loose panicle on a long, slender, reddish-green stalk arising from the base of the pseudobulb between the leaves.

The flowers are about ¾ inch broad, lavender and spotted and striped with purple. The lateral sepals are united at the base forming a small sac. The lip is about as broad as long, deeply notched in the middle with crenulate edges. The capsule is oblong-cylindric, ½ to 1½ inches long, three-ribbed and prolonged at the tip into a beak.

This is a sun-loving orchid growing on the small outer branches of trees at the periphery of hammocks or cypress heads in Monroe and Collier Counties. At places it is extremely abundant, as on some of the interior rivers of the Park where the banks are bordered with hammock hardwoods.

Here *Ionopsis* crowds the sunlit exterior branches or, more often, dangles from the tips of these branches by long slender rootlets. Blooming en masse in March and April, the great numbers of flowers create the illusion of a bluish fog or mist arising from the stream bank — a very striking and attractive display. The plant also blooms sparingly in the fall.

LEPANTHOPSIS
Lepanthopsis melanantha (Reichb. f.) Ames (Fig. D38)

A very small epiphyte 1¾ to 3 inches tall, having several short stems that arise from a mass of spreading fibrous roots and terminate in a single leaf. This stem bears several funnel-form bracts with, hairy margins. The leaf is oval to elliptic, leathery, ¼ to ¾ inch long, and the short, few-flowered raceme arises from its base. The flowers are minute, about 1⁄16 inch wide, reddish purple on short peduncles that

93

arise from funnel-form bracts; the petals and sepals diverge widely. The capsule is ovoid, six-ribbed, and about ⅛ inch long.

This tiny plant has been found in the cypress swamps of Collier County. It blooms in the spring and summer. Little is known about it in Florida. The only specimen seen by the writer was collected in Collier County by Fred Fuchs, Jr. This plant flowered in his greenhouse.

TRINIDAD MACRADENIA
Macradenia lutescens R. Br. (Fig. P18C)

A medium-sized epiphyte consisting of a fusiform pseudobulb up to 1½ inches long, carrying a single leaf at its apex and a drooping raceme or panicle arising from a sheath at the base of the bulb which bears one to a dozen flowers. The single leaf is narrowly elliptic, thick and stiff, one to five inches long, ½ to one inch wide. The greenish-yellow to salmon colored flowers are about ¾ inch wide, diffused with purplish-brown, the sepals and petals are widely spreading; the lip is three-lobed, the lateral lobes embracing the column, the median extended into a slender recurved tongue; the two pollen masses are attached by slender threads widening at the base. The capsule is elongate, fusiform, somewhat three-ridged, ½ to ¾ inch long, and drooping.

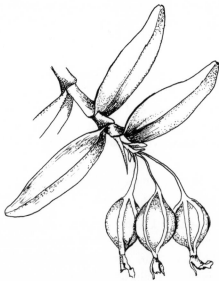

FIGURE D-33. — Umbelled epidendrum. *Epidendrum difforme*. Leaves and seed pods. (natural size).

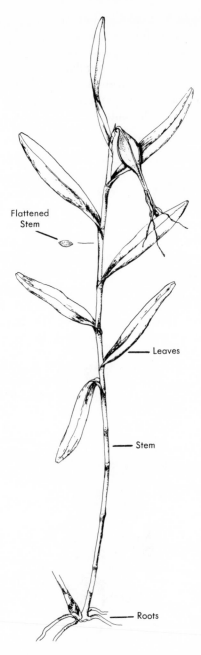

Flattened
Stem

Leaves

Stem

Roots

FIGURE D-34. — Night blooming epidendrum. *Epidendrum nocturnum*. Flattened stem (cross section), leaves and seed pod. (¼ actual size).

This beautiful little orchid is now very rare and possibly exterminated from most of its former habitat. Small reported it abundant on Paradise Key, but no specimens have been seen there in recent years. The flower stalk frequently produces a second or third branch if the first flowers have faded without setting fruit. It blooms persistently from late summer to December. Occasionally a flower stalk is produced from the tip of the bulb.

FIGURE D-35. — Matted epidendrum. *Epidendrum rigidum*. To show plant and seed pods. (⅓ actual size).

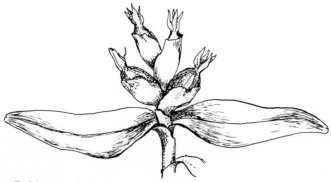

FIGURE D-36. — Strobiliferum. *Epidendrum strobiliferum*. Seed pods and leaves. (2 times actual size).

MAXILLARIA
Maxillaria crassifolia (Lindl.) Reichb. f. (Fig. D39)

A medium-sized plant up to twelve inches tall having the small flattened pseudobulbs concealed by the sheathing leaf bases and several shorter leaf-like bracts. Individual plants clumping together form groups up to ten inches or more in width.

The leaves are V-shaped in cross section at the base and cupped throughout, linear, four to 12 inches long and ½ to ¾ inch wide. One leaf arises from the bulb, two to four clasp its base. The flowers are fleshy, solitary, about 1¼ inches long on a short peduncle, set deeply in and barely projecting from the sheathing leaf base. The sepals and petals are quite similar, oblong-elliptic, partly closed, pale yellow to orange, often marked with purple. The capsule is ellipsoidal, widest below the base, and from ¾ to 1 inch long and fluted.

This species occurs most commonly beyond the boundaries of the Park in the Fahkahatchee Swamp, where it is a fairly common plant. It blooms throughout the year.

SPREAD EAGLE ONCIDIUM
Oncidium carthagenense (Jacq.) Sw. (Fig. P18A)

The flowers are quite similar to those of *O. luridum.* Correll (1950) separates it by the shape of the middle lobe of the lip which, in this species, is not much larger than the lateral lobes, while in *luridum* the mid-lobe is much larger than the lateral lobes. Plants from Central America grown in local greenhouses are predominantly lavender instead of the greenish-yellow to brown of the local *luridum*.

This species is reported by J. K. Small (1933) to have been found in the Cape Sable region. The author has not seen it nor has he been able to obtain any information indicating its present occurrence in southern Florida. It probably cannot be distinguished from *O. luridum* by vegetative characters.

FLORIDA ONCIDIUM, FLORIDANUM
Oncidium floridanum Ames (Fig. D40, P17C)

This plant consists of a mass of white spongy roots about 2 mm. in diameter from which arise long pseudobulbs supporting long linear leaves. The pseudobulbs are 1½ to 4 inches long, 1 to 1½ inches wide, swollen near the base and tapering to the apex on which are borne two slender leaves, often 40 inches long, and ½ to 1½ inches wide, clasping at the base, widest above the middle, and deeply folded for two thirds of their length. Two to four leaves, which are shorter and keeled, clasp the base of the bulb. The inflorescence forms a tall, loose panicle on a slender stalk often seven feet long, arising from the base of the bulb. The flowers are very numerous, about one inch broad on slender pedicels, yellow with greenish to brownish mottling. The sepals and petals are rather similar, elliptic, stalked with crenulate margins and the lip is divided into a broad, medium, yellow lobe notched in the center, with two small basal lateral lobes. The capsule is fusiform, strongly six-ribbed, 1 to 1½ inches long, and about ½ inch thick.

This orchid, also reported from the Bahamas, is conspicuous because of its panicles of showy yellow flowers and long, grass-like leaves. It is most abundant in the hammocks of the Everglades Keys where it is usually terrestrial. It also occurs in the mangrove forests where it is commonly an epiphyte on buttonwood.

The hurricane Donna destroyed most of the plants in the area covered by the tidal wave. When growing as a terrestrial on the thick hammock humus it is readily destroyed by ground fires. It is gradually becoming scarce. Deer frequently eat the leaves and bulbs. Formerly this plant occurred in large colonies and when in flower formed a very attractive display. It blooms in April and May.

MULE-EARED ORCHID, LURIDUM
Oncidium luridum Lindl. (Fig. P12A)

A very large epiphytic orchid, sometimes forming a rosette of leaves well over four feet wide. The pseudobulbs are very small and inconspicuous. The leaves are large, thick, stiff, cupped, oblong-lanceolate, much resembling a mule's ear, sometimes 24 inches in length and six inches wide, often purplish-green in color.

The inflorescence forms a wide, spreading panicle three to six feet tall on a stalk arising from the base of the leaves. The flowers are extremely variable in color, pale green, yellowish-brown or reddish, spotted with darker shades; the blades of both sepals and petals are sub-orbicular and slenderly stalked, with undulate margins; the lip is three-lobed, the middle much larger than the two very small laterals. The capsule is ellipsoidal, two to three inches long and about ¾ inch in diameter, with broad rounded ribs.

This is one of the largest orchids of southern Florida. It was formerly very abundant, but the demand of collectors has reduced its numbers so that it is a very uncommon species except in some very inaccessible locations. Not more than ten years ago there were places where hundreds of specimens of this species could be seen on the

FIGURE D-38 — *Lepanthopsis melanantha*. Plant showing characteristic
stem bracts, one leaf and pods. (natural size).

FIGURE D-37. — Butterfly orchid.
Epidendrum tampense. Plant, bulb
and seed pods. (½ actual size).

FIGURE D-39 — *Maxillaria crassifolia*.
Plant in flower. (¼ actual size).

buttonwoods and pond apples fringing some of the brackish water lakes. These have been decimated. At present it is widely scattered in the area, usually on buttonwoods in the hammocks of the mangrove forests and rarely further inland. It also occurs in the cypress sloughs of Collier County.

Its wide distribution and tenacity should in time, with adequate protection, restore its former numbers and save one of the truly remarkable sights of the area during the blooming period of April and May. The favorite supports are buttonwood, pond apple and cypress. A small bark beetle, *Xyleborus morstatti* (Hopk.), determined by D. M. Anderson, U.S. Department of Agriculture, bores directly into the developing flower stalk and destroys many of the inflorescences in some seasons.

VARIEGATED ONCIDIUM
Oncidium variegatum Sw. (Fig. D41, P16B)

A medium-sized epiphyte with a creeping rootstalk, bearing at intervals groups of four to eight leaves. The pseudobulb is very small, nearly concealed, and the flower stalk projects from its base. The leaves are two to six inches long, rigid, curved and V-shaped in cross section, the margins finely toothed and the bases clasping. The flowers are 1½ to ¾ inches broad, white suffiused with yellow and purple, borne in a simple raceme on the tip of a stalk some six to 12 inches in length. The lateral sepals are fused together, the medium sepal and petals stalked; lip three-lobed with the middle lobe very broad and notched. The column has two prominent petal-like lateral wings at the tip. The capsule is ellipsoidal and ¾ to one inch long.

This species is scarce and not widely distributed. So far as known at present, it is confined to Broward and Palm Beach Counties, where it occurs in drier sandy sites, often among clumps of rosemary (*Ceratiola ericoides*). Mr. Fred Fuchs, Jr., reported it growing on the base of palmettos and oaks or as a terrestrial in the accumulated mixture of sand and humus at the base of these trees. It blooms throughout the year, but most abundantly in March.

PLEUROTHALLIS
Pleurothallis gelida Lindl. (Fig. D42)

A medium-sized plant growing in clumps of a few to 30 stalks, each terminating in a single leaf and the whole from 12 to 18 inches tall. The flower stalk is somewhat shorter than the leaf and clothed with loose bracts. The single leaf is four to eight inches long and ½ to 2½ inches wide, oblong, elliptical, slightly cupped, and slightly keeled on the back of the mid rib, stiff, shiny, yellow-green and rounded at the apex.

The inflorescence is a simple raceme originating from the axile of the leaf and bearing up to 20 small, greenish white, drooping flowers, hardly ¼ inch long. The sepals are hairy, slightly united at the base, especially the two lateral ones, giving a somewhat tubular appearance to the flower. The petals are about half as long as the sepals and the lip is recurved. The capsule is ¼ to ⅜ inch long, ellipsoidal and three-angled.

This plant is distinctive because of the rather large, shiny, single leaf on a slender stem. The tiny pale, fragrant, and inconspicuous flowers are strung along the stalk. It is fairly common in the Big Cypress, but has not been found in the eastern part of the area. It blooms throughout the year.

FIGURE D-40. — Florida oncidium *Oncidium floridanum.* Plant showing bulb and basal origin of flower stalk. (⅙ actual size).

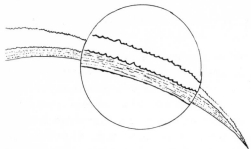

FIGURE D-41 – Variegated oncidium. *Oncidium variegatum.* a single leaf to show serrated edge. (3 times actual size).

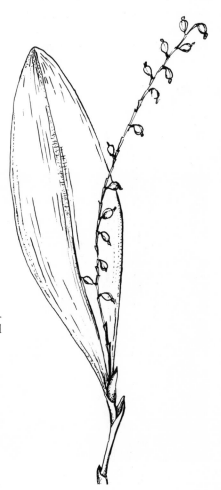

FIGURE D-42. – Pleurothallis. *Pleurothallis gelida.* Shows single leaf and flower spike. (⅓ actual size).

PALE-FLOWERED POLYSTACHYA
Polystachya luteola (Sw) Hook. (Fig. 41, D43, P18D)

A medium-sized erect orchid, five to 18 inches tall, growing singly or, more often, in small clumps. The stem arises from a slightly swollen tapering pseudobulb often indistinct or absent and carrying one to four oblong-elliptic, leathery leaves three to 12 inches long with sheathing petioles. The flowers form in a loose panicle often distinctly one-sided, on a long slightly flattened and keeled pedicel that protrudes from the axil of the leaves. The flowers are small, white to yellowish green, fragrant, about ⅓ inch wide. The two lateral sepals are triangular, the bases broadly united to form a triangular hood partly enclosing the petals. The lip is three-lobed. The capsule is ellipsoidal widest beyond the middle and slightly curved, fluted and ribbed, about ½ inch long.

This is one of the more common species, widely distributed throughout southern Florida in hammocks and shaded sloughs of fresh and salt water areas. It grows on many kinds of trees. The flowers appear from spring to late fall.

FIGURE 40. — Strobiliferum. *Epidendrum strobiliferum.* Plant in flower.

FIGURE D-43 — Pale-flowered polystachya. *Polystachya luteola*. Plant and inflorescence. (½ actual size).

Vanillas

Vanilla Sw.

This is a large genus in the tropics, but only five vanillas have been found in this area. One of these, the vanilla of commerce, has been recently introduced. All species found in Florida occur also in the West Indies. The vanillas are readily distinguished by their vine-like form. These vines climb, or better, ramble over their supports, sometimes to considerable heights. They produce numerous aerial roots, some of which reach to and become rooted in the humus.

They seem to occur naturally or at least most abundantly in the mangrove belt and in the moist hammocks of the East and West coasts (Collier County), but do well in many protected locations when transplanted. They are found climbing most frequently on buttonwood and coco-plum extending their stems up into the sunlight where they flower and fruit. During cold spells the exposed tops are frequently frozen, especially the leafy species.

Two of our species are leafless, two have thick spongy leaves originating at the stem nodes, and one has large thin leaves. The racemes are short and stubby, bearing three to 20 flowers. The flowers are fleshy, the sepals and petals similar in shape, the lip tubular or funnel form and fringed or crenulate at the expanding apex, usually three-lobed. The seed capsule, or pod as it is usually termed in these plants, is long, slender or thick clavate, fleshy, indehiscent or splitting throughout its length in one of our species.

The following key, adapted from Correll (1950) will help to distinguish the five Florida species. Some of the flowers and some of the seed pods of these species have not been seen by the writer.

Key to the Vanilla Orchids

1. Leaves present and of normal appearance 2
   Leaves represented by short, recurved bracts
   or these often wanting 4
2. Leaves thin, strongly veined; pod very
   slender, 5 to 7 inches long .... Thin-leaved vanilla
   V. inodora

   Leaves thick, veins obscure; pods variable 3
3. Flowers more than 2½ inches long; pod thick,
   4 to 5 inches long .... Oblong-leaved vanilla
   V. phaeantha

   Flowers less than 2 inches long, pod fragrant,
   slender, 6 to 10 inches long .... Vanilla vine
   V. planifolia

4. Pod cylindrical .... Leafless vanilla
                                                                V. dilloniana
   Pod club-shaped .... Worm vine
                                                                V. barbellata

LEAFLESS VANILLA
Vanilla dilloniana Correll

This species is recorded from Florida by Buswell (1945) under the name *V. eggersii*, and is said to occur on Big Pine Key, Monroe County. Correll (1950) also records it from Florida in Dade and Monroe Counties. The specimens of this and the following species seen by the writer appear to be the same.

WORM VINE
Vanilla barbellata Reichb. (Fig. D44, P15A, P19C)

This species is widely distributed in southern Florida, along the coast in the Mangrove Belt of Collier, Monroe, Big Pine Key (Dickson, 1953) and Dade Counties. In the buttonwood hammocks of the Flamingo area, it is relatively common and at times forms extensive tangles of green or bronze-orange "ropes" looped through the buttonwood or cocoplum branches. The flowers are fragrant. Buswell (1945) mentions this species under the name *V. articulata*.

The sturdy clavate, often bronze-colored, pod of this species does not split to disperse millions of dust-like seeds into the air like most other native orchids. The seeds are round, hard and heavy for their size, about 1/50 inch in diameter and are suspended in a sticky gelatinous matrix. When ripe, the turgid pods become infested by a small fly that induces fermentation in the matrix causing this gelatinous sticky mass, carrying the seeds, to ooze through punctures made by the insects. This exudation is attractive to, and fed on, by other insects. Probably the seeds adhere to their bodies and are thus carried away.

OBLONG-LEAVED VANILLA
Vanilla phaeantha Reichb. f. (Fig. D45, P19D)

This is the most common and widely distributed of the leafy vanillas of southern Florida. It occurs in the cypress sloughs of Monroe, and Collier Counties and sparingly in the hammocks of the mangrove forests of the Flamingo area. It flowers in June and July.

THIN LEAVED VANILLA
Vanilla inodora Schiede (Fig. D46)

This species with large, thin, conspicuously veined leaves occurs sparingly in the buttonwood hammocks of southeastern Dade County. It is easily overlooked because the leaves closely resemble *Smilax*, a common associate in these hammocks. The long slender pod, five to seven inches long and about ¼ inch thick, is characteristic. The flowers have not been seen by the writer. It was first collected near Florida City, Dade County, by Fred Fuchs, Jr., in 1955.

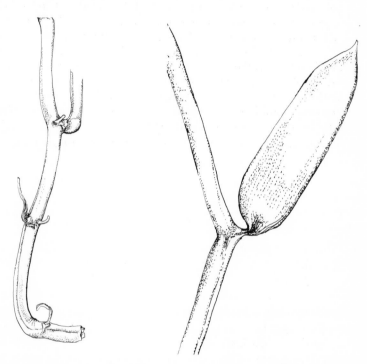

FIGURE D-44. — Worm vine. *Vanilla barbellata*. Portion of stem to show nodes and aerial roots. (½ actual size).

FIGURE D-45. — Oblong-leaved vanilla. *Vanilla phaeantha*. Leaf and portion of stem. (½ actual size).

VANILLA VINE
Vanilla planifolia Andrews (Fig. P19D)

This plant, the common vanilla of commerce (Childers, 1948), has been introduced and grown in southern Florida as a garden plant. It is a much more vigorous vine than the native leafy species with leaves twice its size. Correll (1950) gives an interesting summary of the history and use of this vanilla bean in commerce, from which the following notes are abstracted:

> This 'spice' was first reported by an officer under Cortez when he observed the Aztecs flavoring their drink 'Chocolatl' with 'tlilxochitl' or ground vanilla beans. The source of vanilla was strictly guarded and it was not until about 1510 that the Spaniards discovered the plant and took it to Spain. Its value as a flavoring was soon recognized and it was thought to have medicinal virtues as well. These uses created a strong demand for the beans for over three centuries. With the development of synthetic vanilla, the use of the bean decreased until in the twentieth century it is grown and collected only for special uses, such as in perfumes.

This plant blooms in the summer, from May through June.

FIGURE D-46. — Thin-leaved vanilla. *Vanilla inodora*. Leaf and seed pod. (½ actual size).

Peperomias
Family Piperaceae

The peperomias comprise a large family of plants, chiefly of the tropics, with only a few representatives occurring in southern Florida. Four species from this area have been seen by the writer, all of which are epiphytes. They occasionally are found on the trunks of living trees, but seem to grow best in decomposing vegetable matter or humus, such as the disintegrating bark of logs or knot-holes, and other cavities in living trees. They are low spreading plants, with erect flowering stems arising from creeping rootstalks. They often form a leafy carpet of thick green or reddish-green foliage. They grow in deep shade in moist situations.

Several introduced species are prized as ornamentals for use in rock gardens. The climbing vine (*Piper nigrum*), since very early times has been utilized as the source of the common white and black peppers of commerce. These are made by drying and grinding the fruit. Black pepper is derived from the entire fruit; white pepper from the seed after the exterior coat has been removed. Several other plants of this family are used in the pharmacopoeias of the past. Some of our species are aromatic when dried.

The native species of peperomias are characterized, in addition to their low spreading habit of growth, by tiny greenish flowers thickly set on slender spikes less than ¼ inch thick and one to six inches long. They have no petals or sepals, only a single pistil and two stamens. The fruit is a small, often viscid, berry and in some forms it is beaked.

Key to the Epiphytic Peperomias

1. Flower spike about ¼ inch in diameter; berries
   closely set on stem and bearing a slender
   recurved hook; leaves alternate, leathery,
   usually obovate .... Florida peperomia
                                                       P. obtusifolia

   Flower spike about ⅛ inch in diameter;
   berries distinctly separated on stem,
   sometimes beaked but not recurved 2

2. Plant downy pubescent; stems and leaves
   opposite, reddish-pink; fruit beakless . . . . Reddish peperomia
   P. humilis

   Plant glabrous; leaves alternate 3

3. Plant mainly upright; seeds with a
   flattened beak . . . . Pale green peperomia
   P. simplex

   Plant mostly procumbent; seeds beakless . . . . Cypress peperomia
   P. glabella

CYPRESS PEPEROMIA
Peperomia glabella (Sw) A. Dietr. (Fig. P12C)

This species resembles *P. simplex* but it is much more procumbent and twining, and the stems are often reddish in color. The leaves are decidedly more fleshy, more elliptical, highly glossy and the three veins are indistinct on many leaves. The flower spikes are more numerous, grouped in three to fives at the tip of the stem, and are about as long as those of *P. simplex* but more slender. The berries are not beaked.

This species was recently collected by Dr. Floyd S. Shuttleworth in the eastern portion of central Collier County growing on logs in a cypress slough. It is an attractive species with dark green, fleshy, shiny leaves forming a rather low heavy mat on old logs, but will grow as a terrestrial. It blooms throughout the year.

REDDISH PEPEROMIA
Peperomia humilis Vahl. (P17A)

This plant is much branched, with reddish pubescent stems six to 15 inches tall. The lateral and terminal branches bear slender, greenish yellow flower spikes about ⅛ inch in diameter and two to four inches long. The flowers are slightly separated, at about as much as their width, on the stem.

The fruit is tiny, subglobular, rugose, about one-half the diameter of the spike and beakless. It is not embedded in the spike, but is set on a very short columnar pedicel. The leaves are opposite, pale reddish green, downy pubescent oval and succulent on the earlier shoots. These soon drop off and the subsequent leaves are thinner, ovate and deeply three-veined.

This delicate reddish peperomia occurs sparingly in the mangrove areas, usually protruding from cavities or humus-filled crotches on buttonwood trees. It is reported to occur as a terrestrial on the marl flats of the Cape Sable-Flamingo area but has been seen only on logs or trees by the writer. It blooms at all seasons. When the sunlight filters through the broken buttonwood canopy and falls on these attractive reddish or pinkish-green clumps protruding from a knot-hole, one's

110

progress is effectively halted in admiration. Even the ever-present mosquitoes are forgotten for a moment.

FLORIDA PEPEROMIA

Peperomia obtusifolia (L.) A. Dietr. (Fig. 42, P17A)

A creeping, somewhat shrubby perennial with numerous short upright stems bearing thick, dark-green, shiny, oval to suborbicular, alternate leaves with long petioles. The flower spikes are two to four inches long and about ¼ inch thick, terminating a long stem bearing tiny, closely packed flowers. The smooth, oval fruit is partly imbedded in the spike and terminates in a very slender hooked beak.

This species is common throughout the area in moist, shaded situations. It grows profusely on the lower trunks of living oaks, over dead logs, and as a terrestrial in the humus of the denser hammocks of the pine lands as well as in the mangrove forests and the cypress sloughs. It flowers throughout the year.

It is frequently grown as ground cover in extreme southern Florida and as a pot plant in the north.

FIGURE 41. — Pale-flowered polystachya. *Polystachya luteola.* Plant and flowers.

111

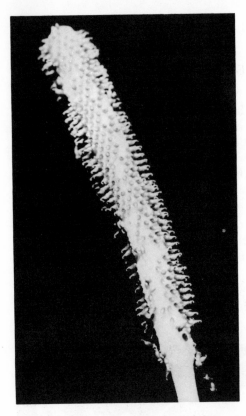

FIGURE 42. — Florida peperomia. *Peperomia obtusifolia.*
Fruiting spike.

PALE-GREEN PEPEROMIA
Peperomia simplex Ham. (Fig. P12C)

A stout erect species, 12 inches to 18 inches tall, stems and leaves
alternate, glabrous. The stems are pale green and the leaves slightly
darker, the latter are fleshy, one to two inches long, usually elliptical
but the lower ones are often ovate. The three veins are not so prominent
as in *P. humilis.* The flower spikes are two to four inches long and
about ⅛ inch in diameter. They usually occur singly, each terminating
a leafy branch and bear tiny globular fruits, separated about the width
of their diameter and borne on a conical base; each fruit terminates in
a flattened, slightly curved beak.

This species was collected in the Fahkahatchee Swamp, Collier
County, growing on stumps and logs, and as a terrestrial by Mr. Fred
Fuchs, Sr. It is more upright and branched than the other species and
blooms throughout the year.

Fig And Mulberry

Family Moraceae

Two native trees, the strangler fig and the shortleaf fig or wild banyan, often start life as epiphytic seedlings on the branches of other trees. They are of tropical origin and belong to a large genus that comprises more than 600 species showing extremely diverse form.

Many species of figs have been introduced into Florida for ornamental use. One of these is a vine which clings tenaciously to walls and fences, especially those made of the rough oolitic limestone. The fig of commerce, *Ficus carica,* is a member of this genus. This relationship can be readily understood if the small fruits of our native species are broken open so as to expose the pulp filled cavity bearing numerous tiny seeds typical of the figs of commerce.

They can be briefly characterized as epiphytic or terrestrial trees with milky sap, alternate entire leaves that are often deciduous in cool weather and with the leaf bud covered with a stipule of the preceding leaf. Long pendulous aerial roots are extended from the branches; these eventually reach the ground and thicken with age to form many trunk-like supports. The tiny flowers are borne inside a hollow receptacle which enlarges into a globular, pulpy fruit.

STRANGLER-FIG
Ficus aurea Nutt (Fig. 43, D47)

This species is commonly epiphytic in the seedling stage. The leaves are large, two to eight inches long, thick, and narrowed at the base, and the length of the petiole is less than half the widest part of the leaf blade. The fruits are sessile, globular, and about ¼ inch in diameter. The height of the tree usually corresponds to that of the forest canopy where it grows, often reaching 60 feet or more.

The sticky seeds of the strangler fig germinate on the limbs of trees, where they are deposited by birds. As the seedling increases in size, an ever-lengthening stem pushes up toward the light where it

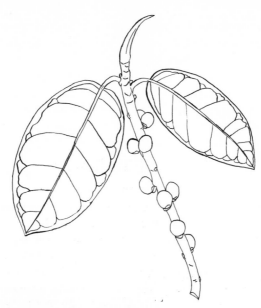

FIGURE D-47. – Strangler fig. *Ficus aurea*. Leaves showing short petioles and sessile fruits. (½ actual size).

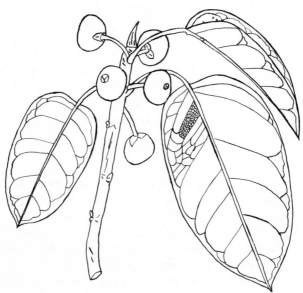

FIGURE D-48. – Banyan tree. *Ficus laevigata*. Leaves showing long petiole and stalked fruits. (natural size).

develops a crown above that of its host. At the same time, long slender aerial roots are extended downward and around the host until they reach the ground, many feet below.

Here true roots extend into the soil and the aerial stems increase in size to a staunch support that gradually encircles the trunk of the host in a strangling embrace. The growth of these massive root-trunks is relentless, slowly but surely the oak or the palm host is compressed and the top dies branch by branch. But this is not the end, for as the trunk of the host decays and falls apart, that of the fig encroaches more and more until even the hollow cavity is occupied by the stem of the fig — the aerial roots have become a trunk.

The strangler fig is a conspicuous feature of the southern Florida hammocks and palmetto stands. It is more common on the palms and live oaks, but also grows on many other trees and occasionally on the roof of a house. The rough walls and chimneys of early Florida homes,

FIGURE 43. — Strangler fig. *Ficus aurea*. Plant growing on a black mangrove killed by hurricane Donna; the fig survived.

built of coral or oolitic limestone, were often cracked and torn apart by the relentless growth of this tree.

Occasionally a large, lone fig stands out as a monument to attest to the former height of some fire-killed hammock. The slow-creeping fire on the humus floor destroys all roots and kills the trees. Although most of the fig's roots may also be destroyed, the crown may live. Other aerial roots are sent down and new supports established to firmly prop the old crown. These living crowns do not topple with the dead trees, but over-top the regenerating sprouts of the new forest by many feet for several years.

WILD BANYAN
Ficus laevigata Nutt (Fig. 44, D48)

This species has smaller, thinner leaves, two to six inches long, broadening at the base, or often somewhat heartshaped, with petioles more than half the width of the leaf blade.

The fruits are about ½ inch in diameter, borne on a short stalk ¼ to ¾ inch in length. The seeds more commonly germinate on the ground, or on stumps, logs or rocks from which aerial roots grow out and down into the soil. In this sense it is not a true epiphyte, but occasionly on cabbage palms it behaves as a strangler fig.

FIGURE 44. — Banyan tree. *Ficus laevigata*. Young fig tree starting on a rock where seed may have been dropped by a bird.

116

Mistletoe Cactus Or Pencil Cactus

Family Cactaceae

One would least suspect a cactus, of all plants, to adjust to an epiphytic habitat. The mere thought of cacti brings to mind visions of torrid desert sands, treeless expanses and long periods of drought. Surprisingly, there are many representatives of this family in southern Florida. They are found mostly on shell mounds and beaches, or on the brackish marl flats among the buttonwood trees. Occasionally an individual plant among these may find a "footing" on an old stump or hollow tree and could be considered an epiphyte. Other forms extend their fluted or rope-like stems, reaching upward many feet into the trees. To all appearances they seems to be epiphytes, but when these aerial portions are served from the roots they slowly wither and die. Only one among our some 20 species has adjusted to this mode of living. This is the pencil cactus or mistletoe cactus.

Many species of this family have an economic importance as ornamentals, some as food for cattle. Others have edible fruits that were eaten by the early Indians. Some were used medicinally, and an exhilarating beverage is reported to be made in the West Indies from a species of *Rhipsalis*.

All our species of cacti are shrubs having a woody framework encased in soft succulent tissue covered by a tough epidermis armed with spines which may represent leaves. True leaves are usually wanting. The flowers are often showy with many sepals, petals, stamens and stigmas. The fruit is a fleshy one-celled berry, usually with numerous seeds.

PENCIL CACTUS, MISTLETOE CACTUS
Rhipsalis cassutha Gaertn. (Fig. P12D)

A drooping shrub with long pendent and succulent, yellowish-green branches up to four feet in length and ⅛ to ⅜ inches in diameter.

The new growth has a few scattered groups of tiny spines that are soon deciduous.

The flowers are very small, white, about ⅜ inches wide, having five wide spreading sepals and petals, ten stamens and three stigmas. The fruit is globular, about ¼ inch in diameter, white, gelatinous, resembling a mistletoe berry. It contains several seeds.

This rare and attractive plant is found sparingly in the mangrove forests near the coast of the Flamingo and Cape Sable regions, usually hanging from buttonwood trees. It has also been recorded from coastal regions in east central Florida.

Some clumps are three to four feet long and nearly as wide. The seedling usually originates in a humus-filled cavity and the plant is supported by strong roots extending into the decaying wood. It flowers in the spring. The attractive, mistletoe-like berries are soon removed and eaten by birds.

Literature Cited

ALEXANDER, TAYLOR R.
  1955 Observations on the ecology of the low hammocks of southern Florida. Jour. Fla. Acad. Sci., Vol. 18, No. 1.
  1958 Temperature variance in microclimates of southern Florida. Proc. Fla. State Hort. Soc., Vol. 71, No. 3.

AMES, OAKES
  1947 Fungi and germination of *Goodyera* Bot. Mus. Harvard Univ. leaflet 11: 1-28

BAKER, MARY FRANCIS
  1949 Florida wild flowers. Macmillan, N.Y.

BIRD, ROLAND T.
  1953 Death trap in a jungle paradise. Everglades Natural History Magazine, Vol. 1, No. 4.

BURNETT, HARRY C.
  1958 Orchid diseases. State Plant Board of Fla. Vol. II, Bull. No. 12.

BUSWELL, WALTER M.
  1937 Orchids of the big cypress. Am. Bot. 43: 147-153.
  1945 Native orchids of south Florida. Bull. No. 3, University of Miami, Coral Gables, Fla.

CHILDERS, NORMAN F. AND HECTOR R. CIBES
  1948 Vanilla culture in Puerto Rico. Circ. No. 28, Federal exp. sta., Mayaguez, Puerto Rico.

CORRELL, DONOVAN S.
  1950 Native orchids of North America. Chronica Botanica Co., Waltham, Mass.

DARWIN, CHARLES
  1877 Various contrivances by which orchids are fertilized by insects.

CRAIGHEAD, F.C. AND V.C. GILBERT
  1962 The effects of Hurricane Donna on the vegetation of southern Florida. Quart. Jour. Fla. Acad. Sci. 25: (1).

DAVIS, JOHN H.
  1943 The natural features of southern Florida. Florida Geological Survey, Bull. No. 25.
DICKSON JOHN D. III, ROY O. WOODBURY AND TAYLOR R. ALEXANDER
  1953 Check list of flora of Big Pine Key, Florida, and surrounding keys. Jour. Fla. Acad. Sci., Vol. 16, No. 3.
HARPER, WILLIAM
  1958 The Travels of William Bartram. Edited by Francis Harper, Yale University Press, New Haven, Conn.
HARRINGTON, H.D. AND L.W. DURRELL
  1957 How to identify plants. Sage Books, Denver, Colo.
HAWKES, ALEX D.
  1947 The epiphytic orchids of Florida. Am. Orchid Soc. Bull. 16: 544-549.
  1961 Orchids; their botany and culture. Harper Bros., New York
MILNE, LORUS J. AND MARGERY MILNE
  1959 Plant life. Prentice-Hall, New York
NEILL, WILFORD T.
  1951 Florida's air plants and their inhabitants. Florida Naturalist, Vol. 24, 3: 61-66.
NOBLE, MARY
  1960 You can grow orchids. New edition. Published by the author, Jacksonville, Fla.
ROBERTSON, WILLIAM B. JR.
  1953 A survey of the effects of fire in the Everglades National Park. National Park Service (mimeograph).
  1959 Everglades — The Park Story. University of Miami Press, Coral Gables, Fla.
SHOEMAKER, JACK
  1958 Spanish moss in Florida. Fla. Dept. of Agric. Bull. No. 85, Tallahassee, Fla.
SIMPSON, CHARLES TORREY
  1932 Florida wild life. Macmillan, N.Y.
SMALL, JOHN K.
  1924 Jour. N.Y. Bot. Garden 25: 53-94
  1929 From Eden to Sahara, Florida's tragedy. Science Press, Lancaster, Pa.
  1931 Ferns of Florida. Science Press, Lancaster, Pa.
  1933 Manual of the southeastern flora. Published by the author.

INDEX

LIST OF ILLUSTRATIONS

COLOR PLATES

NOTES